GERMANIUM

Russian Monographs and Texts
on the Physical Sciences

GERMANIUM

V. I. DAVYDOV

Including
RADIOACTIVE ISOTOPES OF GERMANIUM
by
P. Rudenko and L. V. Kovtun

TRANSLATED FROM THE RUSSIAN
BY
ADAM PEIPERL

GORDON AND BREACH, Science Publishers
New York • London • Paris

CHEMISTRY

Library of Congress Catalog Card Number 66-28891

Printed in the United States of America

TABLE OF CONTENTS

CHAPTER I

IMPORTANCE AND USES OF GERMANIUM IN TECHNOLOGY

In 1871, on the basis of his periodic law, D. I. Mendeleev predicted the existence and described the properties of an element which he called "ecasilicon," an analog of silicon.

It is known of course that D. I. Mendeleev was engaged in experimental chemical studies, trying to find "ecasilicon" in naturally occurring minerals.[1] However, only in 1886 was A. Winkler able to detect in the mineral "argyrodite" an unknown element whose properties coincided with those of "ecasilicon," which had been predicted by the great Russian chemist. The element was called germanium after the name of the country where it was discovered.[2]

As long as the remarkable properties of germanium as a semiconductor were unknown, it was

made in very limited quantities, primarily for research purposes.

As was noted by academician A. F. Ioffe, [3] in
the last decade semiconductors have become the
basis of technological progress in the field of
automation, high-frequency radio engineering, and
current transformation. One of the key positions
among semiconductors is occupied by germanium.

In the near future, science and technology will
undoubtedly face the important problem of the use
of solar energy on a large scale. [4] In the solution
of this problem as well, a leading role will be
played by semiconductors. The use of solar energy
is particularly attractive because, in contrast to
atomic power engineering, it does not result in the
contamination of the earth's atmosphere by harmful
waste.

The development of semiconductor technology has
caused a sharp increase in the production of germanium (Table 1).

Table 1, Production and Consumption of Germanium in Capitalist Countries

Year	Total Production, tons	Of This By Countries, tons	Consumption, tons	Literature Source
1946	0.1	—	—	[5]
1948	0.45	—	—	[6]
1950	0.9	—	—	[6]
1952	2.5	—	—	[5]
1954	18.5 – 20.0	—	10—12	[5, 7]
1956	24.0 – 35.0	USA, 18–20	30	[5, 8]
		Belgium, 10 – 12		} [9]
		Others, 2 – 4		
1958	100	—	—	[10]
1960	—	USA, 24.5	—	[11]

In the Soviet Union also, the industrial production
of germanium has expanded, and it increases
every year with the steadily rising demand for this
semiconductor.

Germanium is used primarily in the manufacture
of semiconductor devices. Diodes and transistors,
which replace vacuum electron tubes, have no in-
candescent filaments, and for this reason require
much less electrical energy while performing the
same functions in electronic devices. Transistors
are small in size, stable toward vibration and im-
pact, and long-lived. Diodes and triodes from a
germanium-silicon alloy (5-6% at.% Si) are characterized by a high thermal stability. At the
present time, the output of germanium diodes and
triodes is measured in tens and hundreds of mil-
lions per year. [11]

Germanium power rectifiers are superseding
those made of selenium, since they have a high
efficiency (99% compared to 80-85% for selenium

rectifiers). Compact germanium rectifiers are now available which permit the passage of currents amounting to tens of thousands of amperes.

The literature[5,12] offers abundant data on the use of germanium and its compounds. Germanium is used in the production of metallized ceramic electrical resistances and powder metal products. Dosimeters of nuclear particles having a resolving time of 0.05 μsec are made by using germanium. Germanium semiconductor devices have been used to convert the energy of radioactive decay into electric energy. Crystal analyzers from single-crystal germanium are employed in x-ray spectroscopy. A film of germanium applied on a reflector has a high reflectivity and good corrosion resistance. Metallic germanium and its dioxide are used as catalysts in certain chemical reactions such as the hydrogenation of coals and chemical nickel-plating. Germanium dioxide is used as a catalyst in oxidative polymerization reactions. Copper-germanium and platinum-germanium thermo-

couples are very sensitive. A germanium-
indium alloy is used in the manufacture of sensitive resistance thermometers operating at low
temperatures. Alloys of germanium with certain
metals are used in radio engineering, instrument
construction, chemical machinery, metallurgy,
and other branches of industry. Germanium
dioxide is an ingredient in the composition of special
types of glasses, particularly those employed in
infrared optics. It is also used in making enamels
and decorative glazes.

Germanium compounds are useful in the activation
of phosphors and luminiphors. Organic germanium
halides find applications in the production of lubri-
cating oils of high technological qualities. Finally,
germanium compounds are employed in medicine
for the treatment of anemia and tuberculosis.

The very incomplete list given above of the areas
of actual and possible applications of germanium indicates its great role in science and technology. In

the last ten to fifteen years, this element has become one of the most indispensable materials.

REFERENCES

1. B. M. Kedrov, Chemistry of Rare Elements, Vol. 1. Moscow, Akad. Nauk SSSR, 1954.

2. B. V. Nekrasov, General Chemistry, Moscow, Goskhimizdat, 1954.

3. A. F. Ioffe, Semiconductors in Modern Physics. Moscow-Leningrad, Akad. Nauk SSSR, 1954.

4. S. A. Shchukarev, Zh. Neorg. Khim., 2, 713-718 (1957).

5. N. M. El'khones, V. P. Aver'yanova and V. N. Maslov, Germanium and Its Compounds (Existing and Possible Fields of Application), Moscow, VINITI, Akad. Nauk SSSR, 1959.

6. J. A. O'Connor, Chem. Eng., 59, 4, 158-160, 290 (1952).

7. D. G. Kochergina, Byull. TsIIN TsM, 13 (66) (1956).

8. Engin. Min. J., 157, 5, 75-78 (1956).

REFERENCES (cont.)

9. Z. I. Trokskaya, Tsvet. Metally, 10, 97-101
    (1958).

10. B. A. Krasyuk and A. I. Gribov, The Semicon-
    ductors Germanium and Silicon. Moscow,
    Metallurgizdat, 1961.

11. F. L. Fischer, Engin. Min. J., 162, 2, 104-
    105 (1961).

12. Concise Handbook on Applications of Rare and
    Platinum Metals. I. S. Stepanova, Editor-in-
    chief. Moscow, TsIIN TsM, Moscow, 1959.

CHAPTER II

MINERALS AND ORES OF GERMANIUM

Germanium is one of the most dispersed elements, although its weight Clarke, according to recent data (1956-1959), is equal to $(1.0-1.5) \times 10^{-4}$.[1-3] The content of germanium in the earth's crust is considerably higher than that of bismuth, antimony, silver, mercury, cadmium and certain other elements, and approaches the content of molybdenum and arsenic.[1,2]

Minerals of germanium are exceptional, but germanium is found in small amounts in the most diverse rocks and ores. Table 2 lists data characterizing the principal minerals and rocks having high contents of germanium.

According to V. M. Goldschmidt, the distribution of germanium among minerals of the earth's crust is determined by processes of three types:

1. Inclusion in the lattice of a crystal if the radius

Table 2, Metals and Rocks Containing Appreciable Amounts of Germanium

Name	Composition	Germanium Content, %	Relation To Other Rocks And Ores
Argyrodite	$4Ag_2S \cdot GeS_2$	7.0	Associated with Argentite, Sphalerite, Fahlerz
Germanite	$7CuS \cdot FeS \cdot GeS_2$	8.7	Included in Polymetallic Sulfide Ores
Renierite	$(Cu, Fe, Ge, As)_x S_y$	7.0	Same
Ultrabasite	$(Pd, Ag, Ge, Sb)_x S_y$	4.0	Found with Quartz, Galena, Proustite, etc.
Cayeuxite Nodules	—	Up to 7.0	Associated with Lower-Cretaceous Clay Deposits
Canfieldite	$4Ag_2S \cdot SnS_2$	1.8	Germanium partly replaces tin

of the germanium ion or atom is close to the corresponding radius of any component of this crystal.

2. When the charges of the ions are different, the substitution proceeds in the direction of formation of more stable compounds. The trapping of germanium in minerals occurs when ions of lower charge are replaced.

3. The process of sorption in sedimentary rocks. An example are sulfides of sedimentary origin containing germanium.

The first two processes are associated with the formation of minerals both from aqueous solutions and from magmas; for instance, the formation of germanite and renierite, and the presence of germanium in silicates.

According to A. E. Fersman,[4] in the depths of the earth's crust and at high temperatures, germanium behaves like a siderophile[1] element; at lower temperatures, it is chalcophile[2] and even lithophile.[3] This explains its dispersity in various geological phases and zones.

[1] Siderophile - associated with iron.

[2] Chalcophile - associated with sulfur.

[3] Lithophile - associated with silicon.

Granite rocks account for 95% of all intrusive rocks, and basalts account for about 98% of volcanic rocks. For this reason, the average content of germanium in granites and basalts reflects its distribution in the earth's crust and practically corresponds to its Clarke. The content of germanium is almost the same in granite rocks, basalts, diabases and gabbro and is close to 1×10^{-4}%. [1]

Despite the fact that the difference in the radii of tetravalent ions of germanium ($0.53 \overset{o}{A}$) and silicon ($0.42 \overset{o}{A}$) in silicates is over 15% (limiting value for isomorphous substitution), these two elements are close from the geochemical standpoint, [1] i.e., under the same conditions they form compounds having similar properties. The substitution of germanium for silicon in silicates is strongly dependent on the nature of the melt. [9]

TABLE 3

Content of Germanium in Various Rocks, Ores and Water

Raw Material	Germanium Content, g/t	Deposit	Literature Source
1. Silicate rocks			
Basic igneous rocks (diabase, basalt)	Average 1.3	USA	(1)
Silicate minerals of igneous rocks	Average 1.0	Norway, Italy, USA	(1-8)
Granites and minerals of granite pegmatites	Average 1.1	USSR (Urals), USA, Norway, East Germany, West Germany, Sweden	(1, 8)
Gabbro	Average 1.1	USA	(1)

TABLE 3 (cont.)

2. Sulfide rocks

a. Rocks and ores of hydrothermal origin

Raw Material	Germanium Content, g/t	Deposit	Literature Source
Polymetallic sulfide ores	1–100 (seldom 1000)	Urals, Siberia	(5, 7, 17)
Copper–lead–zinc polymetallic sulfide ores	30–50	Southwest Africa (Tsumeb mine)	(6)
Zinc concentrates	30–70	USA, Illinois – Kentucky	(6)
Zinc blendes	10–1000	East Germany, West Germany, Czechoslovakia	(8)

TABLE 3 (cont.)

Raw Material	Germanium Content, g/t	Deposit	Literature Source
Tin-containing complex sulfides	Up to 5000		(6)
Sphalerite, pyrite, bornite, chalcopyrite	1–10	Japan, Italy, Austria, Yugoslavia, East Germany, West Germany	(18–22)
Pyrargyrite (Ag_3SbS_3)	Up to 10000	Bolivia	(6)
Enargite (Cu_3AsS_4)	Up to 300	USA	(6)
b. High temperature sulfide ores			
Magnetic sulfide ores	Up to 5	USA (California), Finland, Norway,	(8)

TABLE 3 (cont.)

Raw Material	Germanium Content, g/t	Deposit	Literature Source
Magnetic sulfide ores (cont.)		East Germany, West Germany, Spain	
Nickel and arsenic pyrites	1–10	USA, West Germany	(8)
3. Iron ores			
Iron ores	1–10	USSR (Siberia)	(17, 23)
Magnetic iron ores	5–10 and less	Sweden, Norway, USA	(8)
Iron meteorites	1–500		(1, 8)

TABLE 3 (cont.)

Raw Material	Germanium Content, g/t	Deposit	Literature Source
4. Sedimentary rocks			
Shales	0.8–1.6	USA, East Germany, West Germany	(1, 3)
Clays and clayey minerals	0.5–12.0	USA	(1)
Bauxites	1–10	East Germany, West Germany, France, USA, Chile	(8)
Limestones and sandstones	Up to 0.5	USA	(1)
Sea deposits and clays	1.1–2.0	USA, Pacific Ocean	(1)

TABLE 3 (cont.)

Raw Material	Germanium Content, g/t	Deposit	Literature Source
5. Other raw materials			
Carbonate materials	0.1–1.0	Argentina	(24)
Oxidized nickel ores	0.8–1.7	USSR (Urals)	(25)
Coals	1–100	USSR (Urals, Kazakhstan) East Germany (brown coals), Japan, Great Britain	(8, 26–29)
Petroleum	Traces	USSR	(30)
Wood	In ash 0.01–1.0	Spain	(31)
Hot springs	0.004–0.017	Canada, USA, Japan	(1, 32)

TABLE 3 (cont.)

Raw Material	Germanium Content, g/t	Deposit	Literature Source
Mine waters	Traces	USSR (Urals)	(33)
Sea water	0.05		(1)

A study of deposits formed under high-temperature
conditions (pegmatitic, greisenic, skarnic, etc.)
shows that germanium is associated primarily with
silicates and more seldom with oxides, and thus
displays lithophile properties.

Because of the appreciable solubility of germanium
dioxide in water (4.4 g/l at 20°C), germanium is
washed out of silicate rocks and accumulates in circulating waters. From the latter, it is either
absorbed or penetrates into sedimentary rocks and
sea water.

According to V. M. Goldschmidt,[8] the appreciable
concentration of germanium in nature may be due to
two different processes. First, the accumulation of
germanium in coals as a result of sorption and reduction from circulating waters, or if the germanium
had concentrated in the course of the vital activity
of plants (the germanium concentration in coals may
exceed the Clarke content hundreds of times).
Second, owing to the chalcophile properties of ger-

manium, which are much more pronounced at low
temperatures than at the temperatures of formation
of magmatic sulfides, germanium has enriched
sulfide ores formed at low temperatures from
aqueous solutions. The deposits of minerals rich
in germanium - argyrodite in Saxony and germanite
and renierite in Tsumeb - are typical low-temper-
ature formations. [6]

In sulfide ores, the presence of germanium was
detected both in the form of independent inclusions
of its minerals [10, 11] and in the form of an
isomorphous admixture to the main components of
the ore. [12, 13] Germanium is found more often in
bornite ores of hydrothermal origin and in ores containing sulfo-salts of silver. [3]

In coals, germanium is often concentrated in a
narrow band along the edges of the coal bed. [14, 15]
This is a clear indication of the adsorption of germanium by coals from circulating waters. It was
established that germanium in coals is bound mainly
to the lightest and ashless fractions. [14]

Germanium found in petroleum is both of primary origin (from live organisms) and secondary origin (due to sorption). [16]

Germanium is present in wood, seaweed, mine waters, and hot springs.

The siderophilicity of germanium at high temperatures is shown by its presence in magmatic iron ores and in the iron of meteorites, the germanium content of which sometimes reaches 0.05%. [1]

All of the above principles of the geochemistry of germanium are given in Table 3, which lists the content of germanium in various rocks and ores. The most characteristic and best-studied rocks containing appreciable amounts of germanium are polymetallic sulfide ores of hydrothermal origin and coals.

REFERENCES

1. S.A. El Wardani, Geochemistry of Rare Elements (Collected Papers). Moscow, IL, 1959, pp. 411-434.

2. A.P. Vinogradov, Geochemistry of Rare and Trace Elements in Soils. Moscow, Akad. Nauk SSSR, 1950.

3. A.S. Zhukova, Problems of the Mineralogy, Geochemistry, and Genesis of Deposits of Rare Elements. Transactions of the Institute of the Mineralogy, Geochemistry, and Crystallography of Rare Elements, No. 4. Moscow, Akad. Nauk SSSR, 1960, pp. 174-184.

4. A.E. Fersman, Geochemistry, Vol. 4. Leningrad, GNTIKhL, 1939.

5. E.P. Libman, Industrial Requirements for the Quality of Mineral Resources. Handbook for Geologists, Issue 57, Germanium. Moscow, 1948.

REFERENCES (cont.)

6. Engin. Min. J., 157, 5, 75-78 (1956).

7. S.A. Borovik and N.M. Prokopenko, Izv. Akad.
   Nauk SSSR, ser. geolog., 2, 341-347 (1938).

8. V.M. Goldschmidt, Collected Papers on the
   Geochemistry of Rare Elements. Moscow-
   Leningrad, GONTI, 1938.

9. P.J. Harris, Geochim. et cosmochim. acta, 5,
   4, 185-195 (1954).

10. P. Ramdohr, Fortschr. Mineral, 31, 13-14
    (1952).

11. J.P. Ratledge, J. Ong and J.H. Boyce, Min.
    Engin. 7, 4, 185-195 (1954).

12. H. Kenworthy, A.J. Starliper and A. Ollar, J.
    Metals, 8 (5), sect. 1, 682-685 (1956)

13. F.I. Abramov and A.K. Rusanov, Spectroscopic
    Determination of Germanium, Indium, Cadmium
    and Gallium in Zinc Blendes. VIMS, No. 141.
    Moscow, GONTI, 1939.

REFERENCES (cont.)

14. V.M. Ratynskii, Trudy Biogeokhimicheskoi
    Laboratorii Akad. Nauk SSSR, 8, 183-223 (1946).

15. J. Oka, T. Kanno et al., Bull. Research Inst.
    Mineral Dressing a. Metals, 11, 17-28 (1955).

16. S.M. Kachenkov, Dokl. Akad. Nauk SSSR, 76,
    563-556 (1951).

17. V.S. Domarev, Tsvet. Metally, 9, 23-27 (1938).

18. F. Cremascoli, Ind. mineraria, 1, 83-86 (1950).

19. E. Schroll, Oesterr. Akad. Wiss. Math -
    Naturw. Kl. Aus. 87, 21-25 (1950).

20. K. Kemura, O. Nagashima, K. Saito, M. Shima
    and S. Nakai, J. Chem. Soc. Japan, Pure Chem.
    Sect., 73, 589-591 (1951).

21. K. Morinaga, Bull. Nagauya. Inst. Techn., 4,
    228-231 (1952).

22. P. Ramdohr, Fortschr. Mineral, 31, 13-14
    (1952).

REFERENCES (cont.)

23. G. Laplace, Pubs. inst. recherches, Ser. A,
     41, 61 (1952).

24. M.M. Radice, Ciencia e. invest., 5, 480 (1949).

25. V.I. Davydov, B.V. Teplyakov, P.A. Pazdnikov,
     I.F. Babachanov, V.I. Mikhailov and V.N.
     Balakhnina, Byull. TsIIN TsM, Moscow, 5, 35-
     38 (1960).

26. V.M. Kostrikin, Zh. Prikl. Khim., 12, 10,
     1449 (1949).

27. A.B. Travin, Vost. Fil. Akad. Nauk SSSR, 1,
     44-48 (1957).

28. K. Stenard, Gas J., 274, 4691, 279-280 (1953).

29. V.I. Losev and T.S. Nikiforova, Zh. Prikl.
     Khim., 33, 3, 730-731 (1960).

30. S.M. Kachenkov, Dokl. Akad. Nauk SSSR, 76,
     563-556 (1951).

REFERENCES (cont.)

31. T.U. Laiseca, Forest Phytochemistry. Madrid, 1950.

32. K. Ikada, J. Min. Inst. Kyushn., 23, 12, 582-587 (1955).

33. V.M. Ershov and A.I. Shcheglova, Geokhimiya, 4, 389-391 (1958).

CHAPTER III

RAW MATERIAL SOURCES AND
METHODS OF PRODUCTION OF GERMANIUM

Modern industrial production of germanium is based primarily on the intermediate products and wastes of the processing of polymetallic and zinc sulfide ores and coal. Plants using germanium-containing raw materials recover germanium as a by-product. The scale of its production from polymetallic sulfide ores at separate plants is small and usually does not exceed 2 to 3 tons per year.[1] The production of germanium is organized on a large scale at the Lubumbashi-Kolwezi Plants in the Congo Republic (with the capital at Elizabethville) and Tsumeb (South-West Africa, which ship their germanium di-oxide concentrates to Belgium (Olen) for processing. The capacity of the Belgium plant amounts to over 30 tons of germanium per year.[2] In the USA, ger-manium is obtained as a by-product of the processing of zinc ores.[1]

1. RECOVERY OF GERMANIUM FROM COPPER-LEAD-ZINC SULFIDE ORES

The polymetallic sulfide ores processed by the Tsumeb concentrating plant contain 41 ore minerals.[3] In these ores, germanium is present in the form of two minerals, germanite and renierite, which differ in their flotation properties. The principal mineral is germanite, but it is intimately intergrown with minerals such as galena, tennantite, sphalerite and dolomite,[2] so that in order to sort out the germanium minerals, it is necessary to pulverize the ore down to 20 mμ. Renierite possesses magnetic properties, which are used to determine the quality of the germanium concentrate obtained. The movement of a magnet under glass causes a displacement of renierite, and the rate of this movement (under the microscope) indicates the extent of enrichment of the sample by germanium.

In 1954, the plant adopted a process for separating the germanium concentrate from copper-lead-zinc

concentrates (Figure 1). The copper-lead concentrate, from which zinc has been removed, is stirred
for 10 minutes with a solution of starch and sulfur
dioxide at pH = 5.2 in a conditioning tank. The
rougher flotation of germanium is then carried out,
most of the metal being removed as a frothy product
from the first three chambers. The concentrate of
the rougher flotation is treated with limestone for
10 minutes and recleaned in an open cycle at
pH = 10.0-10.5. The rougher germanium concentrate is thus obtained. The tailings of rougher and
recleaner flotation consist of the copper-lead concentrate. Table 4 shows the recovery indices of
germanium.[4] The recovery of germanium in the
concentrate amounts to over 28% for an enrichment
by a factor greater than seven. The concentrate
obtained in the plant, containing 0.20-0.45% germanium, is shipped for further treatment to the former
radium plant at Olen, Belgium.

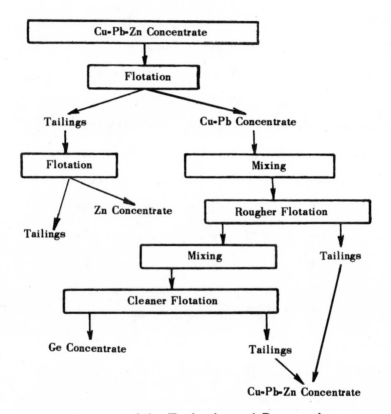

Fig. 1, Diagram of the Technological Process for
Producing Germanium at the Tsumeb Plant

During the first few years, the Tsumeb germanium
concentrates were treated at Olen by the wet process
(Figure 2). The oxidizing roasting of the concentrate
was carried out in reverberatory furnaces. Sub-
sequent leaching of the sinter caused up to 90% of the
germanium to go into solution. The leaching was
carried out in two stages. The concentration of sulfuric acid in the solution after the second stage of
leaching was 50 g/l, whereas after the first stage it
was 5-10 g/l. The solution, containing 5.6 g/l germanium, was evaporated until the concentration increased tenfold, and was cooled with vigorous stirring. Germanium tetrachloride was then distilled
out of the thick slime obtained. The wet process was
simple and was carried out with standard equipment.
However, the production losses were high and the
recovery was not sufficient.

In a number of American laboratories, studies were
carried out for the purpose of developing a process
that would be more suitable for the treatment of the
germanium flotation concentrate. [2] Three processes

were proposed and tested on a small scale. Two are
based on the use of caustic soda for leaching germanium: one involves leaching in an autoclave; the
third, preliminary pelletizing and sintering on a belt.
The third process is based on the volatilization of the
sulfides, followed by the extraction of germanium
into the condensate and distillation of germanium
tetrachloride.

The Belgian company which treats the germanium
flotation concentrate also developed a new process
using a vertical retort for volatilizing the sulfides
(Figure 3). The temperature of the retort process is
determined by the requirement of minimum losses in
the sublimates. In an atmosphere of carbon monoxide
or flue gas at a temperature of about $900^{\circ}C$, the volatilization of germanium sulfide reaches 90-93%, and
that of lead sulfide, 5-10%. After drying to a moisture
content of 2%, the charge is briquetted. Prior to
charging into the retort, 4% wood charcoal or 10% coke,
relative to the weight of the concentrate, is added to the

briquets. This increases the porosity of the charge
and prevents its fusion.

The vertical retort furnace is an open-flame muffle
furnace with a built-in retort made of carbon brick.
The briquets are charged periodically from above by
means of a charging mechanism and are lowered into
the reaction zone. The gas obtained from wood
charcoal (average composition: 28-30% CO, 1-2%
H_2, balance nitrogen) is passed through the retort
from the top downward. The gases containing the
volatilized sulfides are passed through a water-cooled
condenser and cloth dust-collectors. The sulfide
residue is discharged through a mobile feeder into a
closed container.   The average temperature of the
reaction zone is 870-980°C, and the gas temperature
is 700°C. The sublimate collected from the con-
densers and dust collectors is roasted in electric
furnaces. The roasting is conducted at 550°C in
order to oxidize as much of the sulfur as possible,
and to drive off the arsenic as the trioxide. The

GERMANIUM

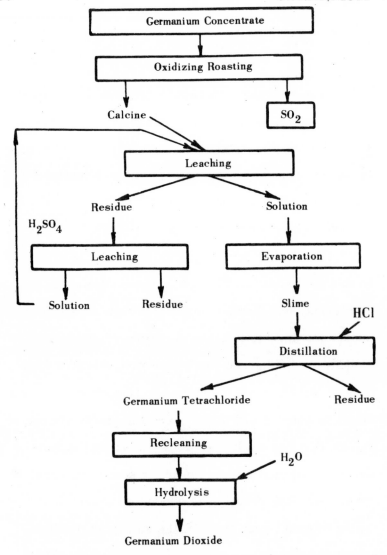

Fig. 2, Diagram of the Hydrometallugical Processing of
Germanium Concentrates at Olen (2).

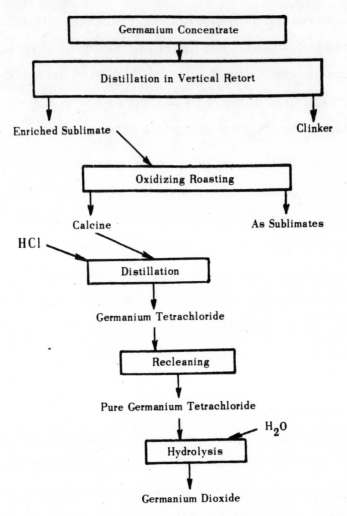

Fig. 3, Diagram of the Pyrometallugical Processing of Germanium Concentrates at Olen.

oxide residue is treated, then germanium tetrachloride is distilled. Results of the treatment of germanium concentrates by volatilization of the sulfides are shown in Table 5. The total recovery of germanium by the plant using this process is 90%.

Whatever the manner in which they were obtained, the germanium concentrates are subjected to distillation in which germanium is driven off as the tetrachloride. The distillation process is carried out with a 9 N hydrochloric acid solution in the presence of chlorine. The latter is necessary to oxidize the arsenic, and also antimony and bismuth. If the chlorination is carried out without free chlorine, arsenic trichloride (boiling point 130°C) is volatilized together with germanium tetrachloride (boiling point 83°C). The chlorination is conducted in an insulated vessel. The primary stills are glazed steel boilers of 200-liter capacity with steam jackets provided with stirrers and discharged through the bottom. The lids have holes for Pyrex distillation columns and inlets

Table 4, Recovery of Germanium at the Tsumeb Plant in July, 1954.

Product	Yield, %	Content, %			Recovery, %		
		Cu	Pb	Ge	Cu	Pb	Ge
Initial Copper-Lead Concentrate	100	11.83	56.60	0.053	100	100	100
Germanium Concentrate	4	26.54	23.30	0.385	9.07	1.59	28.12
Copper-Lead Concentrate	96	10.72	57.94	0.039	90.93	98.41	71.88

Table 5, Distribution of Elements in the Processing of Germanium Concentrates.

Product	Yield %	Content, %			Distribution %		
		Ge	As	Pb	Ge	As	Pb
Germanium Flotation Concentrate	100.0	0.25	7.5	26.0	100	100	100
Sulfide Calcine	85.0	0.024	0.15	28.8	8.3	1.7	94.2
Oxide Residue	2.7	8.5	32.2	55.5	91.5	1.1	5.7
Arsenic Sublimate	9.7	0.005	75.0	0.15	0.2	97.2	0.1

for chlorine and the acid. At the start of the operation, the material is charged into the still and mixed
with concentrated hydrochloric acid and various circulating solutions. Chlorine is introduced without
being preheated until it saturates the solution, then
germanium tetrachloride is distilled in a moderate
stream of chlorine. The vapors condense in a Pyrex
condenser cooled to -10° by circulating brine. The
condensed tetrachloride is collected in 75-liter
Pyrex flasks provided with mechanical stirrers and
is subjected to chemical purification. Each still-
condenser-collecting vat-cleaning bottle train oper-
ates as an independent unit. In order to prevent the
loss of tetrachloride, each vat containing $GeCl_4$ is
connected to a condenser in which the temperature
is $-10^{\circ}C$. All the effluent gases are washed with
sodium carbonate in a tower of 1.2 m in diameter and
6.5 m high. The spent solution is periodically re-
cycled.

The chlorination compartment contains rubber-
lined settling tanks with a mechanical stirrer for the

treatment of the various by-products. Germanium is recovered from the latter by neutralizing the hydrochloric acid solution with limestone.

Germanium tetrachloride is purified in a separate section of the plant where the oxide is produced. All of the equipment in this section is made of quartz or a special plastic. Following chemical purification, germanium tetrachloride is subjected to fractional distillation.

When germanium dioxide is precipitated by hydrolyzing the purified tetrachloride, the stirring, the rate of addition of the tetrachloride to doubly distilled water, and the temperature of the process are closely controlled. After filtration and washing, germanium dioxide is dried at 200°C in an electric furnace.

Of major importance in the production of semiconducting germanium is the maintenance of a high degree of purity in the course of the production process; this is accomplished by using special

structural materials and by taking special pre-
cautions against external contaminants. All the
working areas are provided with forced ventilation.
An "absolute" filter of high efficiency for small sizes
of the trapped particles is used to purify the air.
Particularly high requirements are set for the purity
of the air used to force the liquids into the bottles.
The floors, walls and work clothes in the
sections of germanium oxide production are covered
with a special composition. The paint used for
coating the metal parts of the equipment must not
contain any inorganic dyes. The water is purified
in ion-exchange columns filled respectively with
activated carbon and cation- and anion-exchange
resins. The specific resistance of the water thus
obtained is 5×10^{6} ohm/cm. The preparation of
germanium metal and its refining will be discussed
below.

The copper-zinc sulfide ores of the Republic of the
Congo are characterized by a high content of ger-

manium. Rich copper ore (up to 20% Cu) and copper
flotation concentrates are treated by the copper
smelting plant in the town of Lubumbashi (near
Elizabethville). [1,2] In certain Katanga ores, germanium is found in the form of inclusions in the mineral renierite. In selective flotation, renierite is
primarily associated with copper minerals. For
this reason, following selective flotation, the bulk of
the germanium present in the copper-zinc sulfide
ores of the Republic of the Congo is subjected to
smelting with copper concentrates.

The copper smelting plant at Lubumbashi has an
annual capacity of 120,000 tons of crude copper. [1]
The main technological process of the plant includes
sintering, semipyritic smelting of the sinter in shaft
furnaces, and purging of the matte in the converter.
In shaft smelting, germanium distributes itself between the matte, the slag and the dust. The matte is
fed into the converter, where part of the germanium
excapes with the dust. The slags of shaft furnaces,
containing zinc, cadmium and germanium, are stored.

The metallurgical dusts trapped by the cloth dust-collectors consist of a complex raw material containing zinc, cadmium and arsenic. They are shipped for treatment to a zinc electrolysis plant located in the vicinity, in the town of Kolwezi.

The dust-processing plant in Kolwezi was put into operation in 1955; its planned capacity is 590 tons of dry dust per month. The annual output is 220 tons of dry concentrates containing 8-10% germanium or 25-31 tons of germanium dioxide. The average recovery of germanium from the processing of dusts is about 75%; the after-treatment recovery by sintering attains 92%, and leaching and precipitation produce over 80%. A flow diagram of the dust-processing plant is shown in Figure 4.

Prior to sulfate roasting, the dusts are mixed with sulfuric acid (60-100% of the weight of the dust) and water on a screw feeder. The mass has a moisture content of 25-30%. The sulfating is carried out in a rotary furnace 1 m in diameter and 22 m

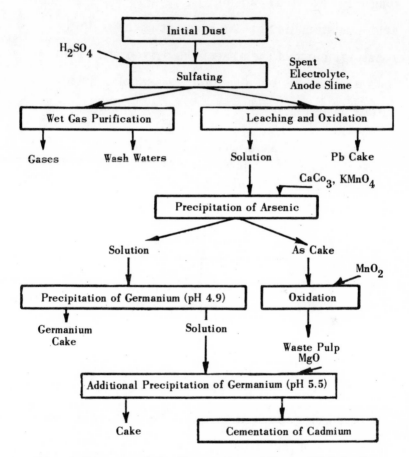

Fig. 4, Diagram of the Processing of Dusts Rich in Germanium at Kolwezi.

long for 4 hours at 450-500°C. The furnace has an acid-resistant lining. As a result of the sulfate roasting, most of the arsenic is driven off. Table 6 lists data on the loss of elements associated with sulfate roasting.

Table 6, Data on the Sulfate
Roasting of Dust at the
Kolwezi Plant.

Element	Content in dust, %		Loss Due to Roasting, %
	Initial	Roasted	
Germanium .	0.36	0.285	8
Zinc .	28.0	22.5	6
Cadmium .	3.0	2.64	5
Lead .	25.0	20.3	3
Copper .	1.5	1.2	—
Arsenic .	7.3	0.7	88—90

Before being discharged into the atmosphere, the gases leaving the furnace are washed in scrubbers. The cake is transferred into a hammer mill in order to pulverize the lumps formed.

The leaching is carried out in agitators (each having a 42-m^3 capacity) lined with lead for 1.5 hours.
At the same time, 9-10 tons of the charge is introduced. Leaching involves the use of a sulfate solution consisting of a mixture of the spent electrolyte
from the electrolysis of cadmium and of wash waters
from the filtering operation at the last stages of the
process. The final acidity of the solution is 10-15
g/l, and its composition at the end of the leaching is:
110-130 g/l Zn, 15-20 g/l Cd, 2.5-4 g/l As, 1.4-2
g/l Ge, 2-4 g/l Cu. The average recovery by leaching is 98-99% Zn, 94-96% Cd, 80-85% As, 90-95%
Ge, 75-90% Cu and 78-80% Fe. After the pulp has
settled, an oxidizing agent is added to the clarified
solution. The pressed pulp is filtered on filter
presses. The residue is a lead cake (61.5% Pb,
1.28% Zn, 0.5% Cd, 0.83% Cu, 0.39% As, 0.05%
GeO_2).

The oxidizing agent used is anodic slime from
electrolysis, which contains a large amount of
manganese dioxide. In order to complete the oxida-

tion, excess potassium permanganate is added. The
oxidation operation lasts 1.5 hours at 45°C. The
oxidation is accompanied by a partial precipitation of
arsenic in the form of arsenates of iron and other
metals; the arsenic concentration drops to 1.5-2.0
g/l. At this stage of the process, the solution is adjusted to pH 2.3-2.4 by the addition of pulverized
limestone. The pulp is filtered and washed on filter
presses, then the solution is sent to the section where
germanium is precipitated. The arsenic content of
the solution is less than 0.4 g/l, that of iron 100
mg/l, and that of copper 3-5 g/l.

Germanium is precipitated in two stages. At first,
only a part of the germanium is precipitated, in order
to obtain a purer product. In the first precipitation
of germanium, magnesium oxide is added until the
pH is 4.9. The second stage of precipitation is
carried out at a higher pH, and the precipitate is returned to the preceding stage. The cake obtained
from the first stage of precipitation contains 8-10%

Ge, 15-20% Zn, 1-1.5% Cd, 10-18% Cu, 0.7-2.0%
As. This product is dried and shipped to the refining
plant at Olen.

The low-grade germanium precipitate obtained
from the second stage is concentrated and shipped
without filtration to the cadmium cementation section
of the zinc electrolysis plant. Its composition is:
110-120 g/l Zn, 12-18 g/l Cd, 1-3 mg/l As and
15-36 mg/l Ge.

The copper-zinc sulfide ores of the Kipushi deposit
of the Republic of the Congo contain germanium in
the form of inclusions of the mineral renierite,
which has ferromagnetic properties. Renierite is
easily floatable in the main cycle of copper sulfide
flotation. The initial ore contains 0.022%, and the
copper concentrate, 0.13% germanium. [6]

Semicommercial tests have shown that the magnetic separation of the copper concentrate can produce a concentrate with a germanium content of
0.919%. Magnetic periodic-action separators are

used for this purpose. The pulp is introduced from
the top and passes through a set of screens. Acted
upon by the strong magnetic field created by a sole-
noid with a direct current of 16 A at 110 V, the magnetic particles are attracted and held firmly against
the screen. When the electric power is shut off, the
concentrate falls into a receiver. The output of one
separator is 5.5 m^3/hr of a pulp containing 1350
kg/m^3 of solid matter.

The concentrate obtained is fused in an electric
furnace and 85-90% germanium is recovered in the
form of sublimates of sulfide and monoxide containing 4-9% germanium. Arsenic and about 20% of the
lead and zinc present in the concentrate are carried
off with the sublimates.

The zinc ores of the USA also serve as a source
material for the industrial production of germanium.
Given below is a description of the technological
process used in the production of germanium at a
zinc plant in Vermont, [2] where from 4.5 to 7 kg of

germanium dioxide is obtained daily. The main raw
material used by this plant are zinc concentrates
whose germanium content reaches 400 g/t. The bulk
of the concentrates contains 40-100 g of germanium
per ton. The average content may be assumed to be
100 g/t.

In the course of the oxidizing roasting and sintering
of the concentrate, most of the cadmium, germanium
and lead concentrate in the fumes and dust; these
products are processed by the cadmium plant.
Cadmium and zinc are leached out by a weak acid
solution. Germanium is leached out of the lead cake
with hot concentrated sulfuric acid, and is then
precipitated as a sulfide cake. After oxidizing
roasting, the cake is washed away from the cadmium
by acid, and germanium tetrachloride is distilled
(Figure 5).

Another plant where germanium is obtained from
zinc concentrates, located in Henrietta (Oklahoma),
belongs to the Eagle-Picher company.[5] Here

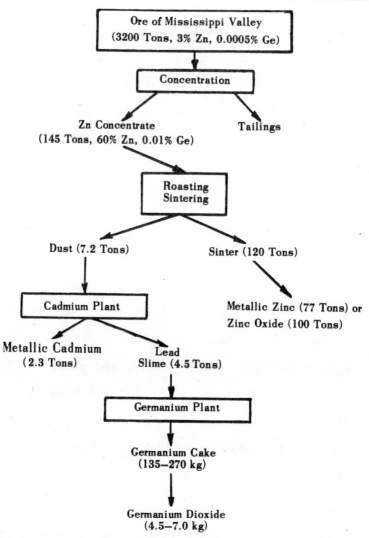

Fig. 5, Daily material flow at the Vermont plant.

(Figure 6), the zinc concentrates are roasted in order
to oxidize the sulfide. Coal and sodium chloride are
then added to the calcine, and the sintering is carried
out at a high temperature. Cadmium chloride and
germanium chloride are vaporized; the sublimate is
then subjected to further treatment. [7]

Of interest is the technology of the side recovery
of germanium at the lead-zinc plant complex of the
Vieille Montagne Co. in Balen (Belgium). [8] The
bulk of the germanium is introduced into the cycle
with intermediate products of the zinc production
which contain from 10 to 400 g of germanium per ton.
The lead plant receives imported concentrates, cakes,
and secondary raw materials. The zinc plant of this
complex processes imported concentrates and also
zinc sublimates from the fuming unit of the lead
plant. [1]

A certain amount of germanium passes into a
weakly acidic solution when the zinc calcine is
leached and is precipitated as a pure cake. Its bulk,

however, remains in the solid residue from leaching
and is subjected to the fuming process. During the
lead smelting, germanium in the form of germanates
passes almost completely into the slag together with
zinc. By subjecting the residue from the leaching of
zinc calcines and slags of lead smelting to the fuming
process, it is possible to convert up to 70% of zinc
into sublimates. A significant part of the germanium
also sublimes as the monoxide. Germanium is ac-
cumulated by recycling certain intermediate products,
as shown in Figure 7.

Thus, sublimates from the fuming process contain
up to 0.1% germanium. Removal of germanium
from the cycle results in a certain decrease of the
germanium content in the intermediate products,
but it still remains sufficiently high for recovery
purposes. Germanium is removed from the closed
chain of the process at the stage where its concentration reaches a maximum. Such a stage is the
leaching of zinc out of the fuming-process sublimates,

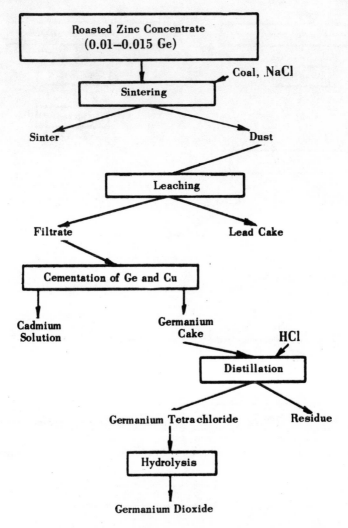

Fig. 6, Diagram of The Recovery of Germanium From Zinc Concentrates.

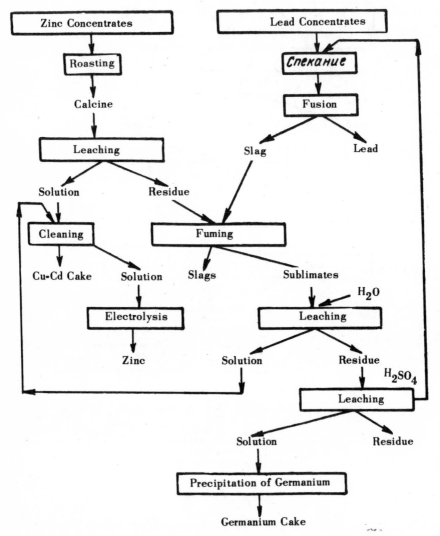

Fig. 7, Diagram of The Recovery of Germanium at Balen.

the residues of which contain up to 0.3% germanium.
Leaching of these residues with sulfuric acid permits
the dissolution of germanium, which is then precipitated from the solution as a hydrated cake in which
its content is 2-3%. Distillation of the cake yields
the tetrachloride, whose purification and hydrolysis
produce pure germanium dioxide. The dioxide is
reduced to metallic germanium at the plant complex.

2. RECOVERY OF GERMANIUM FROM COALS AND PRODUCTS OF THEIR PROCESSING

Germanium is present in substantial quantities in
the coals of all the coal-bearing areas of England,
with the exception of South Wales.[9] The average
germanium content of coals is 7 g/t. When the coals
are burned, a certain concentration of germanium in
the ash takes place. As was noted above, the germanium content of certain ashes reaches 60 or even
130 g/t. However, the gasification of coals is associated with a considerably greater concentration
of germanium in the dust collected from the flue

gases. As a rule, the germanium content of the
latter is twelve times as high as that of ashes resulting from the burning of coal. In certain dusts of gasworks, the germanium content attains 0.072-
0.156%.[9] These dusts contain an appreciable
quantity of gallium (up to 0.3%). A method of re-
covering raw metals from dusts of gas plants which
has found industrial applications in England is
described in the literature.[5,7,9] The dust contains
iron, oxides of silicon and aluminum, and also
readily sublimable elements - lead, zinc, arsenic.
Iron is a good collector of germanium. The dust is
fused with the addition of soda and limestone in order
to flux the oxides of silicon and aluminum, and also
with the addition of copper oxide and carbon in order
to extract gallium with copper. Fusion at high temperature forms copper-iron reguli. If the sulfur content of the initial dusts exceeded 5%, the dusts are
subjected to preliminary oxidizing roasting. This
excludes the possibility of the formation of a matte,
which absorbs the copper and thus reduces the re-

covery of gallium. The copper-iron reguli contain
up to 3-4% germanium in a direct recovery of 90-95%.
The content of gallium in the reguli is 1.5-2.0% in a
50-60% recovery. An additional 20% of gallium can
be recovered by remelting the slag obtained with
copper oxide and coal dust. Germanium which did
not pass into the reguli is carried off for the most
part by the gases and deposits in the flue of the
furnace. The flue is periodically cleaned and the
dust is returned into the process.

The dissolution of the reguli upon passage of gaseous chlorine through the solution proceeds with the
evolution of heat and does not require any external
heating. The rate of the reaction is controlled by
the amount of the chlorine passed. A dilute solution
of iron perchlorate serves as the catalyst of the
reaction. Germanium tetrachloride is volatilized
from the solution obtained and subjected to fractional
distillation to remove most of the arsenic. The final
removal of traces of arsenic is carried out in a col-

umn packed with pure copper turnings. Hydrolysis
of germanium tetrachloride produces a dioxide containing only traces of arsenic (less than 1 part per
10^7 parts of germanium).

Germanium also has been found in the ammonia
liquid of the Tokyo gasworks,[9] where an experimental plant with an annual capacity of 500 kg of
germanium was put into operation.

3. RECOVERY OF HIGH-PURITY METALLIC GERMANIUM

We shall briefly discuss the problems involved in
the production of germanium of semiconductor
purity which have been discussed in detail in the
monograph of B. A. Krasyuk and A. I. Gribov.[10]

Most plants producing metallic germanium reduce
pure germanium dioxide with hydrogen.[7,8] The
reduction is sometimes carried out with ammonia
obtained from coking. A method of reducing germanium tetrachloride by zinc vapors of high purity
is known.[7] However, in this case germanium is

bound to be contaminated by traces of zinc. The
temperature of the process of reduction of germanium dioxide by hydrogen is maintained around 650°C.
Thus, losses of germanium due to volatilization of
the intermediate reduction product, germanium
monoxide, do not exceed 2 to 3%.[2] The reduction
is conducted in graphite boats placed in a tubular
electric furnace. A discontinuation of the evolution
of water indicates the complete reduction of the germanium dioxide. Oxygen is removed from the hydrogen used for the reduction by passing the hydrogen
through palladized asbestos, absorption of the moisture by silica gel, and freezing out with liquid
nitrogen.

The reduced germanium is a dark-gray powder.
To fuse it, the temperature in the furnace is raised
to 1000°C. At first, instead of hydrogen, purified
nitrogen or some other inert gas is passed through
the tube in order to raise the quality of the ingot. If
the fusion is conducted in hydrogen, the ingot obtained
is porous, since the fused germanium dissolves hy-

drogen relatively well, and the latter escapes during
solidification and forms pores. The germanium
reguli obtained have a resistivity of the order of 3-5
ohm cm, which indicates the presence of a substantial quantity of impurities. Pure germanium has
a resistivity of about 60 ohm cm at room temperature.
In the preparation of semiconductor devices, alloyed
germanium is used, i.e., germanium containing a
given quantity of atoms of certain chemical elements.
For this reason, the starting material to be alloyed
must be germanium with a resistivity of no less than
40-50 ohm cm. Germanium of this kind can be
obtained only by using physical purification methods,
i.e., directional crystallization and zone melting.

In the directional crystallization of the germanium
melt in a boat, the crystallization front moves
slowly from one end of the boat to the other. The
impurities, which are less soluble in solid that in
liquid germanium, are driven to the end of the ingot,
which is the last to solidify. [2] The melting is carried out in a graphite boat at 1030°C in an atmosphere

composed of 95% nitrogen and 5% hydrogen, and is subjected to directional cooling at a displacement rate of the ingot of 20 cm/hr. About 10% of the ingot must be cut off in order to eliminate the impurities.

In zone melting, the germanium ingot contained in a quartz or graphite boat and placed in an inert gas atmosphere or in a vacuum is slowly moved past a narrow hot zone created by induction heating or by a resistance furnace. A local fusion of germanium thus occurs, and the molten zone travels along the entire length of the ingot. The impurities concentrate in the liquid phase and, as the molten zone moves along, are displaced toward the end of the ingot. In order to achieve a sufficient degree of purity of the germanium, the zone melting process is repeated several times and even dozens of times. The traveling rate of the molten zone is usually 12-36 cm/hr. Depending upon the type of conduction required (n- or p-type), pure germanium is alloyed by adding metals of group III or V of the periodic

table. This is done in the last operation, i.e., the
growing of single crystals. The first semiconductor
germanium diodes were made from polycrystalline
material. Soon, however, it was established that
the major properties of semiconductors depend not
only on their content of certain impurities but also
on the perfection of the crystalline structure. For
this reason, it was necessary to develop methods of
preparing large single-crystal ingots containing a
minimum number of structural defects and sufficiently homogeneous in their chemical composition.

In industry, germanium single crystals are prepared by Czochralski's method (growing the single
crystal by withdrawing it from the melt and using a
single-crystal seed). Zone melting in a horizontal
boat or vertical floating zone melting is used much
less frequently for this purpose because these
methods do not always provide single crystals of the
desired quality.

In practice, the cooling of single crystals by the Czochralski method is carried out in the following manner: Fragments of zone-refined polycrystalline germanium which have been etched for the purpose of purification are immersed in a crucible made of spectroscopically pure graphite. A single crystal seed is inserted into the seed holder mounted on a vertical rod. The working volume of the furnace is then made airtight and evacuated to a pressure of 10^{-4} to 10^{-6} mm Hg. The germanium is melted by means of a resistance element, i.e., a graphite heater, or by induction heating. After the fusion and some overheating, the temperature of the melt is adjusted slightly above the melting point of germanium (936°C). Rotation of the crucible promotes the maintenance of a uniform temperature in the melt. The seed is lowered until it touches the melt and, after it has begun to fuse, the lifting mechanism of the upper rod on which the seed holder is mounted is turned on. As the seed rises, germanium crystallizes on it. An ingot which is gradually pulled out of the

melt is thus formed; it consists of a germanium
single crystal having the same crystallographic ori-
entation as the seed. The rotation of the rod with the
seed holder prevents warping of the ingot in the course
of the crystallization.

Recently, attempts have been made to use salt melts
to protect molten germanium from contamination and
purify the finished single crystals. The extraction of
copper from germanium with molten potassium cyanide
has been carried out. A two-hour treatment of single-
crystal wafers measuring 20 x 10 x 2 mm increased
their resistivity from 2-3 to 3-5 ohm/cm.

Other experiments have demonstrated the feasibility
of growing germanium single crystals with a resistivity
up to 10-15 ohm/cm under fluxes with a boron oxide
or potassium chloride base of chemically pure or
analytically pure grade. [11]

The molten-salt phase may suppress the influence of
foreign crystallization seeds and partly protect the
molten germanium and the growing crystal from
oxidation.

REFERENCES

1. Nonferrous Metallurgical Plants of the Capitalist Countries; a Concise Handbook. Moscow, TsIIN TsM, 1958.

2. Engin. Min. J., 5, 78-88 (1956). Probl. Sovr. Metallurg., 2, 46-62 (1957).

3. M.A. Fishman and D.S. Sobelev, Practice in the Beneficiation of Ores of Nonferrous and Rare Metals. Part. 1. Beneficiation of Polymetallic Ores. Moscow, Metallurgizdat, 1957.

4. J.P. Ratledge, J.N. Ong and J.H. Boyce, Min. Engin., 7, 4, 374-382 (1955). Ref. Byull. TsIIN TsM, No. 1, 39-40 (1956).

5. T.A. O'Connor, Chem. Engin., 59, 4, 158-160 (1952).

6. L.Ya. Shubov, Tsvet. Metally, 4, 93 (1961).

7. O. Rösner, Probl. Sovr. Metallurg., 5, 90-101 (1955).

REFERENCES (cont.)

8. T. Boving and J. Andre, Probl. Sovr. Metal-lurg., 4, 78-81 (1959).

9. J.A. Gay, Chem. and Pros. Engin., 36, 6, 175-179 (1953).

10. B.A. Krasyuk and A.I. Gribov, The Semiconductors Germanium and Silicon. Moscow, Metallurgizdat, 1961.

11. V.N. Maslov, Yu. V. Granovskii and V.D. Samygin, Zh. Prikl. Khim., 32, 11, 2571-2574 (1959).

CHAPTER IV

PHYSICOCHEMICAL PROPERTIES OF
GERMANIUM AND ITS COMPOUNDS

1. POSITION OF GERMANIUM IN THE PERIODIC TABLE

Germanium is located in the fourth period of group IV of the periodic system. Its atomic weight is 72.6, and its atomic number, 32.

From the standpoint of its physicochemical properties, germanium belongs to the group of semimetals such as carbon in the form of graphite, silicon, gallium, gray tin, black phosphorus, arsenic, antimony, bismuth, and tellurium.[1] Germanium is considered to be an element with properties intermediate between those of semimetals and metals.[2] Being at the boundary between metals, which conduct electric current, and nonconducting metalloids, germanium combines the properties of both of these groups and is a semiconductor. It can form both anions and cations. In its properties, germanium is closer to silicon than to tin. The atomic radius of germanium is also close to the atomic radius of silicon. [3] The atomic radii of elements with co-ordination number 12 are given below in Å:

Silicon 1.34
Germanium . . . 1.39
Tin 1.58

The radii of tetravalent anions are 2.71 Å for silicon, 2.72 Å for germanium, and 2.94 Å for tin. The radii of tetravalent cations differ more appreciably: silicon 0.41 Å, germanium 0.53 Å, and tin 0.71 Å. Accordingly, the similarity between germanium and silicon is greater in their compounds with metals (in the anionic form) and less pronounced in compounds with metalloids, germanium and silicon being in the cationic form.

The ion of divalent germanium is similar in properties to the ion of divalent tin. [3]

2. ELEMENTAL GERMANIUM

Germanium has a silver-gray color with a metallic luster. It crystallizes in the cubic system with a diamond-type lattice. The unit cell is 5.62 Å.

Only stable isotopes are found in nature, and in the following proportions:[2] with mass number 70 – 20.4%, 72 – 27.4%, 73 – 7.8%, 74 – 36.6%, and 76 – 7.8%. Artificial unstable (radioactive) isotopes with mass numbers 66, 67, 68, 69, 71, 72, 73, 75, 77, 78 are known.[1]

Table 7 lists the values of the atomic and ionic radii of germanium for various types of compounds.

Table 7, Atomic and Ionic
Radii of Germanium,
Å (1)

Ge^{4-}	$Ge^{\circ}_{at.}$	Ge^{2+}	Ge^{4+}
2.67	1.01	0.69	0.44
2.72	1.29	0.73	0.52
2.83	1.473	0.93	0.53
—	—	0.98	0.54
—	—	1.27	0.58

In compounds with coordination number 4, the radius of the tetravalent germanium cation is 0.50-0.55 Å, and in those with coordination number 6, 0.53-0.58 Å.

The bond energy of crystalline germanium is 42 kcal/g-atom. Its density at $25^{\circ}C$ is 5.32 g/cm^3. The variation of the density of germanium with the temperature is given below:

Temperature, $^{\circ}C$	960	980		
Density, g/cm^3	5.571	5.565		
Temperature, $^{\circ}C$	1000	1050	1100	
Density, g/cm^3	5.557	5.532	5.505	

Reported values for the melting point of germanium differ. However, the most reliable value for the melting point of germanium should be taken as $1210.2^{\circ}K$ (205).

A characteristic feature of semimetals is the fact that they frequently occur in several modifications. This also applies to germanium. Both amorphous and crystalline germanium are known. When heated to $350-400^{\circ}C$, germanium is transformed from the

amorphous state into the crystalline state.[8] During
the transformation, germanium with coordination
numbers 4 and 12 in the first and second coordination
sphere is formed with almost identical lattice parameters.

According to various sources, the entropy of
crystalline germanium at 25°C is equal to 10.14, [7]
10.1 ± 0.2; 11.3, [1] and 7.432 ± 0.015 cal/deg
g-atom. [9]

The handbooks[1,7] give values of the heat of melting of germanium: 7.13 ± 0.35 kcal/g-atom of germanium containing up to 0.4% oxygen; the values
8.1 ± 0.8 and 8.3 kcal/g-atom are given for pure
germanium. The experimentally determined values
of the entropy of melting of germanium are 4.94-
6.74 cal/deg g-atom. [1,7]

The heat capacity C_p of metallic germanium with a
resistivity of 10 ohm cm in the range of 600-900°C
is equal to 0.08-0.085 cal/g deg;[1] for 25°C, the
value of 0.086 cal/g deg or 6.24 cal/deg g-atom is
given. [2,7]

Values of the heat capacities of crystalline germanium were measured in the range of 2.5-300°K. At temperatures above 20°K, the measurement error did not exceed ±0.2%.[9] The results of these measurements are shown in Table 8. The heat capacity of metallic germanium at 25°C is probably close to the average value of 5.9±0.3 cal/deg g-atom.

The temperature dependence of the heat capacity of crystalline germanium, obtained by calculation, is given by the formula[10]

$$C_p = 5.90 + 1.13 \times 10^{-3} T \text{ cal/deg g-atom.}$$

The heat capacity of liquid germanium is approximately equal to 7.5 cal/deg g-atom.[10]

The thermal conductivity of metallic germanium changes from 0.37 to 0.156 cal/cm sec deg in the range of 90-300°K. Samples of p-type germanium have a higher thermal conductivity than n-type samples.[23]

The viscosity of pure germanium at 940-1250°C was studied during heating and cooling.[24] Figure 8 shows the dependence of the dynamic viscosity of germanium on temperature.

The vapor pressure of liquid germanium at 1237-1609°C was determined by means of Knudsen's effusion method.[10] The technique of this method was described in.[11,12]

In the experiments of,[10] use was made of graphite crucibles whose lids had apertures 0.175 and 0.336 cm in diameter. The germanium vapor escaping from the hole condensed on a water-cooled platinum collector. The data obtained from the experiments are shown in Table 9 and are graphically illustrated in Figure 9.

A mathematical treatment of the experimental data gave the following dependence of the free energy on the temperature of vaporization of liquid germanium:

$$\Delta F_T = 87490 + 2.0\ T \log T - 45.5T.$$

Table 8, Heat Capacity of Crystalline Germanium.

T, °K	2.5	10	50	100	200	300
C_p, cal/deg g-atom	0,0001413	0,01394	1,479	3,302	5,033	5,590
$C_p - C_v$, cal/deg g-atom	—	—	—	0,001	0,011	0,023

Table 9, Vapor Pressure Over Liquid Germanium.

Tons, °C	p, mm Hg	Tons, °C	p, mm Hg	Tons, °C	p, mm Hg
1237	$1,01 \cdot 10^{-3}$	1372	$8,72 \cdot 10^{-3}$	1473	$4,07 \cdot 10^{-2}$
1254	$1,49 \cdot 10^{-3}$	1376	$1,08 \cdot 10^{-2}$	1522	$8,34 \cdot 10^{-2}$
1334	$4,43 \cdot 10^{-3}$	1400	$1,34 \cdot 10^{-2}$	1555	$1,16 \cdot 10^{-1}$
1342	$4,56 \cdot 10^{-3}$	1482	$1,81 \cdot 10^{-2}$	1609	$2,63 \cdot 10^{-1}$

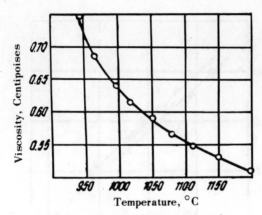

Fig. 8, Dynamic Viscosity of
Germanium Versus Temperature

The heat of vaporization of germanium obtained
for standard conditions (25°C) H_{vap} = -84.0$\pm$1.5
kcal/g-atom, the heat of fusion ΔH_{fus} = -8.3
kcal/g-atom, and the boiling point is 2687°C.

Mass-spectrometric studies showed that the germanium atoms can be associated in vapors.[13]
Table 10 lists the heats of vaporization of certain
associates.[13]

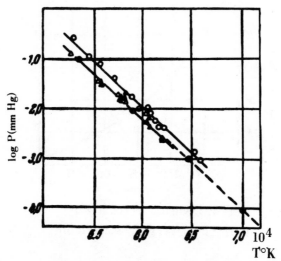

Fig. 9, Vapor Pressure Over
Liquid Germanium Versus
Temperature (as given by var-
ious authors).

Later data, [14] obtained by an integral modification
of Knudsen's method from the weight loss of the
graphite chamber containing the substance and simultaneously from the twisting force of a filament
acted upon by the jet stream of the escaping
vapor, showed lower vapor pressure values than
those given in ref. [10] The experiment established

Table 10, Heats of Vaporization
of Germanium, kcal/mole.

t, °C	Ge_1	Ge_2	Ge_3	Ge_4
1150	89 ± 2	—	—	—
1400	79 ± 2	83 ± 2	81	70

that in the range of 1335-1612°C, the molecular
weight of the germanium vapor escaping from the
hole was 58 $\pm$ 16, i.e., that the vaporization involves primarily monatomic molecules. The results of these investigations are shown in Table 11.

The heat of vaporization of germanium at 25°C
calculated from these data is equal to 91.7 $\pm$ 0.3
kcal/g-atom.

Data on the rates of sublimation and vaporization of
germanium in the range of 847-1635°C are listed
below:

Table 11, Vapor pressure Over Liquid Germanium

t, °C	$p \cdot 10^3$ mm Hg		t, °C	$p \cdot 10^2$ mm Hg	
	from the weight loss	from the twisting force		from the weight loss	from the twisting force
1335	0,262	0,258	1445	1,63	1,59
1372	0,447	0,714	1453	2,02	1,60
1378	0,537	0,813	1507	3,75	3,75
1440	1,67	2,27	1509	3,47	3,69
1440	1,57	1,86	1612	13,50	12,70

Temperature, $^{\circ}$C	Rate of vaporization, g/cm^2 sec
847	1.45×10^{-7}
996	1.4×10^{-6}
1112	1.34×10^{-5}
1251	1.27×10^{-4}
1421	1.21×10^{-3}
1635	1.14×10^{-2}

In addition to the boiling point of germanium cited above, the literature contains the following data: 2627, 2687, 2700, 2707[1] and 2610°C.[4] The value of 2700°C has been adopted.

A very high vaporization rate of germanium was observed in tellurium vapors which was considerably in excess of the vaporization rate in a vacuum.[18] As shown in Figure 10, the vaporization rate of germanium at 900°C increases linearly with increasing pressure of tellurium vapor up to 1 mm Hg. Above this value, the vaporization rate becomes independent of the vapor pressure of tellurium. The

transition to saturation is not yet completely under-
stood.

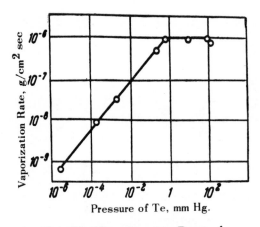

Fig. 10, Vaporization Rate of
Germanium Versus Vapor Pressure of Tellurium at 900°C.

The heat of vaporization of germanium calculated
from experimental data in tellurium vapor at a pressure of 0.6 mm Hg. is 12.7 kcal/mole, which is 7
times less than the heat of vaporization of germanium in a vacuum.

For comparison, Figure 11 shows the temperature
dependence of the vaporization rates of germanium

in tellurium vapor at a pressure 0.6 mm Hg[15] and
in a vacuum.[10]

It is possible that the vaporization of germanium
is due to the formation of germanium telluride. The
latter apparently dissociates at a high temperature
prior to condensation, since the sublimate consists
of germanium crystals with a very small admixture
of tellurium.

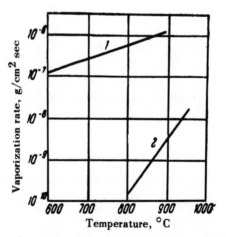

Fig. 11, Temperature Dependence
of The Vaporization Rate of Germanium in Tellurium Vapors.

1— pressure of 0.6 mm Hg; 2— in vacuum.

Experiments on the vaporization of germanium in vapors of selenium and tellurium have shown that in this case the vaporization rates of germanium are even higher than in the case of vaporization in a vacuum, but appreciably lower than in tellurium vapors. Electron diffraction and chemical analysis have shown that finely dispersed sublimates which form during the heating of germanium in selenium and sulfur vapors are chemical compounds of germanium with selenium and sulfur, respectively.

The problem of oxidation of metallic germanium by oxygen at high temperatures has been investigated fairly thoroughly. [16, 17] Thus, a study of the oxidation rate of germanium in the range of 575-705°C at an oxygen pressure considerably below atmospheric has shown that the process can be followed by means of the weight loss of the sample. [16] In the absence of oxygen, after 4 hours' exposure at 800°C and a residual pressure of about 10^{-6} mm Hg, the loss was only 0.1 mg/cm^2 for the test sample. However, in the oxidation

of germanium, the weight of the sample decreased
by several milligrams per square centimeter. This
may be explained by the formation of the volatile
monoxide on the germanium surface. As will be
shown below, of the two germanium oxides, monoxide and dioxide, the former is appreciably volatile
at temperatures as low as 650-700°C, whereas the
latter becomes appreciably volatile only above
1150-1200°C.

A film of monoxide is always formed at the very
start of the oxidation of germanium. However, the
vaporization rate of germanium monoxide decreases
as the reaction proceeds, owing to the formation of
an impervious film of germanium dioxide.

A study of the oxidation rate of germanium at
450-700°C showed that above 550°C the oxidation
rate increases with decreasing oxygen pressure. [17]
This is illustrated in Figure 12. Indeed, as the
oxygen pressure decreases, all of the germanium
monoxide formed on the surface manages to sublime,

GERMANIUM

i.e., reactions (a) and (b) take place, the rate of reaction (c) being very low

$$Ge + 1/2\ O_2 \longrightarrow GeO\ (s)\ ; \qquad\qquad (a)$$

$$GeO\ (s) \longrightarrow GeO\ (g)\ ; \qquad\qquad (b)$$

$$GeO\ (s) + 1/2\ O_2 \longrightarrow GeO_2\ (s). \qquad\qquad (c)$$

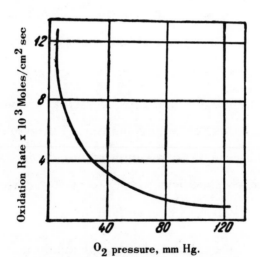

O$_2$ pressure, mm Hg.

**Fig. 12, Rate of Germanium Oxidation
Versus Oxygen Pressure at 550° C.**

When the oxygen pressure increases, the oxidation proceeds according to reactions (a) and (c),

i.e., reaction (c) begins to prevail over reaction (b).
After a continuous film of germanium dioxide has
formed on the surface of the sample, the reaction
rate is determined by the rate of diffusion of oxygen
and germanium monoxide through this film, and the
oxidation process slows down considerably.

The initial stage of oxidation of the germanium surface has been thoroughly studied.[18] The surface of the
sample is first reduced at 600°C with carbon monoxide
in order to remove any bound or adsorbed oxygen.
The oxidation is conducted at an oxygen pressure of
75 mm Hg and at temperatures from 25 to 400°C.
The first oxide layer, which contains one oxygen
atom per germanium atom, is formed in less than
1 min. At temperatures above 250°C, the formation
of the second oxide layer also proceeds fairly
rapidly. However, further oxidation slows down
considerably. Thus, a germanium dioxide film
only 17.5 Å thick formed in 3 hours at 400°C.

A similar pattern of oxidation of metallic germanium
is observed not only at lower oxygen pressures but
also at low partial oxygen pressures in mixtures of
gases with a total pressure of 1 atm. On heating to
800-850°C in a stream of nitrogen containing about
1% oxygen, small samples of powdered germanium
were converted into the sublimate to the extent of
94-95% in one hour. [19] The collected sublimate is
close to germanium monoxide in its composition.

An appreciable volatilization of germanium in a
stream of carbon dioxide was observed at 850°C. [20]
The formation of germanium monoxide in accordance
with the reaction

$$Ge \text{ (s)} + CO_2 \longrightarrow GeO \text{ (s)} + CO$$

was also observed in this case.

Below 500°C, the oxidation of germanium by carbon
dioxide practically does not occur. [21] Above 600°C
a reaction begins, forming germanium monoxide,
which sublimes. As the temperature is raised, the
reaction rate increases sharply, as is evident from
the data of Table 12. [21]

Table 12, Decrease in The Weight of Single-Crystal Germanium Having a Resistivity of 6 ohm cm During Reaction with Carbon Dioxide.

t, °C	Weight Decrease, mg/cm² After a Reaction Of			t, °C	Weight Decrease mg/cm² After a Reaction Of		
	Hours	4 Hours	8 Hours		Hours	4 Hours	8 Hours
600	0,18	0,55	0,71	850	62,1	115,6	215,5
700	2,17	4,5	9,1	875	66,0	130,5	252,0
750	6,2	11,0	20,0	900	76,0	511,0	—
800	35,3	71,0	125,0	970	108,0	—	—

A brief exposure of germanium to air at room
temperature causes the formation of a monolayer of
the composition GeO on the surface of the sample;
prolonged exposure leads to the formation of a
monolayer of the composition GeO_2. When water
vapor is adsorbed on a germanium surface covered
with an oxide film, the passivating properties of the
latter are impaired, resulting in the formation of a
thick layer of oxides. [22]

Krypton coats metallic germanium with 0.15 to 2.0
monolayers at temperatures of 77.8°K and 82.3°K
and pressures of 10^{-4} to 4 mm Hg. [32]

In the liquid state, germanium has a close-packed
structure with coordination number 8, whereas the
coordination number in the crystal lattice of germanium is 4. This is confirmed by experimental
data on the increase in density associated with the
fusion of germanium. Thus, the structure of liquid
germanium differs much more from the structure
of its solid state than is the case with typical metals.

Elements with covalent bonds such as diamond, silicon and germanium are characterized by an exceptional brittleness at room temperature. Experiments have shown that germanium of 99.999% purity displays an appreciable plasticity at 600°C and a pronounced plasticity at 700°C in bending, compression and extension. [25] Small single-crystal bars 10 mm long and with a cross section from 1 to 3 mm^2 can be bent at 800°C at an angle of almost 180°. Numerous slip lines appear in this case.

It has been noted that germanium is plastic at 670° and brittle below 550°C. [26] A germanium crystal can be extended linearly by 20% at 700°C.

In, [27] a considerable softening of germanium was observed at temperatures above 650°C. Some sort of transformation probably takes place in the structure, and new glide planes appear. Germanium, brittle at 20°, acquires plastic deformability above 900°C. As the melting point was approached, a sharp increase in strength was observed due to the appearance of plastic deformability.

It has been noted that under pressure, a polymorphic transformation takes place in metallic germanium. [28]

The temperature dependence of the surface tension of germanium was studied by means of the method of maximum pressure in a gas bubble in the range of 980-1400°C. [29] The precision of the determinations was 1%, which did not exceed 7 erg/cm^2. The relation obtained can be expressed by the formula

$$\sigma = 621.4 - 0.261 \, (t - 936^{\circ}C).$$

where σ is the surface tension, erg/cm^2;

t, the temperature, $^{\circ}$C;

936°C, the melting point of germanium;

621.4, the surface tension of germanium at the melting point, erg/cm^2.

In other investigations dealing with the determination of the surface tension of germanium, [30] a sessile drop on a graphite or quartz base was photo-

graphed in a vacuum. The experiments involved
single-crystal germanium with a resistivity of 40
ohm cm. The precision of the data obtained was
$\pm 5\%$. The surface tension around the melting point
was 650 erg/cm^2. In the case of a quartz base, it
decreased linearly as the temperature rose and
amounted to 530 erg/cm^2 at 1200°C. In tests with a
graphite base, the surface tension increased from
600 erg/cm^2 at 1000°C to 720 erg/cm^2 at 1200°C.

The difference in the signs of the temperature coefficient of surface tension in the determinations on
a quartz and graphite base is apparently due to the
influence of small amounts of impurities.

The diffusion of certain elements (Li, Cu, Zn, B,
Ga, In, P, As, Sb, Fe, Ni) in germanium has been
studied.[31] It was found that the activation energy
of the process of diffusion of copper in germanium
was 0.18 eV.

The activation energy and the preexponential factor
for self-diffusion in germanium are respectively
equal to 3.2 eV and 87 $cm^2/sec.$ [34]

A relationship is observed between the catalytic
activity and the electronic properties of semiconductors. In the presence of n- and p-type germanium,
a study was made of the reaction between an organic
halide and a benzene derivative. [35] The reaction is
more complete when p-type germanium is used.
Independently of the conduction type, the extent of the
reaction increases as the resistivity of germanium
decreases.

Data on the chemical etching of germanium are
available. Figure 13 shows the change in the dissolution rate of n-type germanium in hydrogen peroxide at about 100^oC. The change in the pH of the
medium has a pronounced effect on the dissolution
rate. Hydrogen peroxide containing a certain amount
of free alkali (at pH 7-8) has a stronger effect on
germanium. [36]

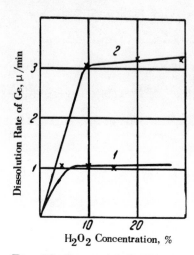

Fig. 13, Rate of Solution of Germanium Versus Hydrogen Peroxide Concentration:
1— at pH = 4–5; 2— at pH = 7–8

The dissolution of germanium in hydrogen peroxide may be treated as a three-stage process; oxidation of germanium to the monoxide, i.e., formation of a monolayer of oxygen on the surface, oxidation of the monoxide to the dioxide, and dissolution of germanium dioxide in water. If an alkali hydroxide is present in the solution, sodium germanate passes into the latter. The rate-determining step is probably the dissolution of germanium dioxide.

In other studies,[37] the weight loss of the samples was used to determine the dissolution rate of germanium in water and in a 3.4% solution of hydrogen peroxide saturated with ozone. The conditions of the experiment were as follows the temperature was maintained within $\pm 1°$; pH = 5; ozone content 0.77×10^{-3} mole/l at $15°$ and 0.52×10^{-3} mole/l at $25°$C; the germanium samples had a resistivity of 2 ohm cm.

Figure 14 shows the results of the investigations.
The activation energy of the process of dissolution of
germanium in the 3.4% solution of hydrogen peroxide
is 11 kcal/mole, and in a solution saturated with ozone,
2 kcal/mole.

The dissolution rate of single-crystal germanium in
nitric acid was studied as a function of the concentration, rate of stirring and temperature. [38]

The dissolution rate of germanium depends on the concentration of undissociated nitric and nitrous acid.
Since nitrous acid is formed in the course of the reaction of germanium with nitric acid, the process of
dissolution is autocatalytic (Figure 15). Hence, stirring at concentrations below 6 N HNO_3 decreases the
dissolution rate because of the elimination of the reaction products from the germanium-nitric acid interface.

In a dissolution without stirring, the dissolution
rate reaches a maximum at a concentration of nitric
acid of 6 N.

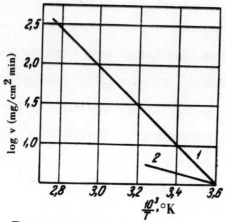

Fig. 14, Dissolution Rate Of
Germanium Versus Temperature:
1—in 3.4% solution of hydrogen peroxide;
2—in water saturated with ozone.

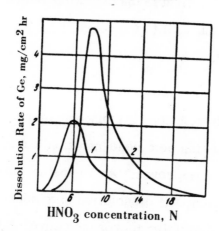

Fig. 15, Dissolution Rate Of Germanium Versus Nitric Acid Concentration at 27.5 °C.
1—without stirring; 2—with stirring (390
rpm)

The dissolution potential of n-type germanium is more positive than that of p-type germanium. At the same concentration of nitric acid, p-type germanium dissolves more rapidly. The dissolution process is determined by the reaction of the cathode (reduction of nitric acid) and the dissolution potential associated with the anodic reaction.

The presence of hydrofluoric acid in weak solutions of nitric acid does not affect the dissolution rate of germanium until its concentration becomes high enough (about 6 N) to decrease the dissociation of nitric acid.

In nitric acid solutions with concentrations above 6 N, the dissolution rate of germanium decreases with increasing acid concentration and increases as the stirring improves. At a constant nitric acid concentration, the dissolution rate decreases with time and eventually approaches zero. The higher the concentration of nitric acid, the faster the germanium surface becomes passivated. The time re-

quired for the passivation may vary from several
hours to a few seconds. The passivation is determined by the surface oxide film (germanium dioxide).
The average thickness of the oxide film varies from
a few microns to 150 Å.

The interaction of germanium with nitric acid solutions at concentrations above 6 N is controlled by
the anodic reaction (formation of germanium dioxide),
and the passivity is related to the anodic polarization.
A decrease in the solubility and solution rate of germanium dioxide with increasing nitric acid concentration plays a primary role in the passivation
process. The passivation of germanium in concentrated nitric acid solutions may be prevented or
removed by adding hydrofluoric acid, which dissolves the protective oxide film.

Germanium is practically inert toward water and
nonoxidizing electrolytes in the absence of dissolved
oxygen at temperatures up to $100^{\circ}C$. [39]

In oxygen-saturated water, the dissolution rate of germanium at room temperature is close to 1 $\mu g/cm^2$ hr. [40]

The curve representing the dissolution rate versus the concentration in electrolyte solutions has a peak (Figure 16). At pH less than 6, this factor does not affect the dissolution rate of germanium. As the pH rises, the dissolution rate increases. The interaction of germanium with electrolytes such as dilute solutions of potassium halides, sodium nitrate and sulfate, and cesium, barium and lanthanum chlorides has been studied. In the range of concentration from 10^{-6} to 1.0 N, the dissolution rate passes through a maximum. The concentration corresponding to the maximum dissolution rate is different for different electrolytes, but is always less than 10^{-2} N.

The activation energy of the process of dissolution of germanium in solutions of potassium chloride saturated with oxygen is 19 kcal/mole.

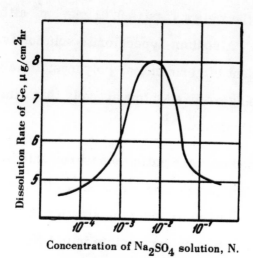

Concentration of Na_2SO_4 solution, N.

Fig. 16, Dissolution Rate Of Germanium Versus Sodium Sulfate Concentration.

In the reaction with fused sodium peroxide, the dissolution rate of germanium with a resistivity of 3.5 ohm cm is 15 mg/cm^2 after 5 min, 26.6 mg/cm^2 after 10 min, and 54.2 mg/cm^2 after 15 min. [21] In a 20% solution of potassium permanganate at room temperature, the weight loss of the germanium sample 10 minutes after the start of the dissolution

is 0.016 mg/cm^2, and 0.033 mg/cm^2 after 60 min.
At 100°C, the weight loss is 0.01 mg/cm^2 after one
minute.[21] A sodium hypochlorite solution is a
strong oxidant of germanium, polycrystalline germanium being oxidized more actively than single-
crystal germanium.[21]

The method of polarization measurements by
means of thin germanium electrodes with p-n
junctions was used to study the kinetics of the anodic
dissolution of n-type germanium in 0.1 N HCl in the
presence of reductants.[41] The experiments showed
that the acceleration of the reaction involved in the
dissolution of germanium upon the addition of reductants of the type of $C_2O_4^{2-}$ and I^- is explained primarily by an additional influx of holes from the in-
terior of the semiconductor to its surface. This
influx is induced by the action of the electric field
arising from the injection of electrons into germanium during the oxidation of the reductants.

The behavior of germanium in the multielectrode system Ge - In - Sn - Cu was studied in a 1 N solution of NaOH containing various amounts of hydrogen peroxide and in pure hydrogen peroxide.[42] In this multielectrode system, germanium acts as the anode, copper is the most effective cathode, and tin and indium are strongly polarized and are either cathodes or anodes, depending upon the conditions. However, the total loss of n-type germanium in contact with copper, indium, and tin is determined by the rate of its anodic dissolution and spontaneous dissolution. The relative magnitude of these rates depends on the composition of the electrolyte. As the hydrogen peroxide content in the solution increases, the loss of germanium due to spontaneous dissolution also increases. These data are used as a basis for the determination of the conditions of etching of crystals with p-n junctions in the manufacture of diodes and other devices prepared from germanium.

As is evident from the data presented above, the
type of conduction of germanium appreciably affects
the rate of the electrode processes. Thus, in the
case of p-type germanium, the cathodic reactions of
the reduction of Fe^{3+}, H_2O_2 and the discharge of
hydrogen atoms are strongly inhibited, whereas in
the case of n-type germanium, the process of its
anodic dissolution is hindered. [43]

It has been noted that the dissolution of germanium
takes place on local portions of the surface which
are anodes, whereas the oxidizing agent is reduced
on local cathodic portions. [44]

The adsorption of atoms of phorphorus, copper,
silver, antimony, indium and gold on the surface of
germanium from aqueous solutions was studied by
means of radioactive isotopes. [45] It was found that
the adsorbed atoms of copper, silver, indium and
gold practically are not removed from the germanium
surface even when the samples are treated repeatedly
with boiling doubly distilled water. The density of

the adsorbed layer is 10^{16} -10^{18} atoms per cm^2 of germanium surface at concentrations of these impurities of 10^{-5} -10^{-2} in the solution.

In order to study the adsorption of cations of sodium, calcium and iron in the course of the etching and washing of germanium samples, use was made of the radioisotopes Na^{24}, Ca^{45} and Fe^{59}. [46]

In a 28% solution of hydrogen peroxide, the magnitudes of the adsorption of these cations are similar and attain 10^{-6} -10^{-5} g-atom/cm^2 of the germanium surface.

A study was made of the sorption of germanium in solution in the form of germanic acid and of the anion $HGeO_3^-$ on aluminum hydroxide. [47] It was shown that 5 minutes after the precipitate came in contact with the solution, the sorption of germanium amounted to 99% at a ratio Al:Ge = 100 and temperatures of 20-80°C. The initial content of germanium in the solution based on germanium dioxide was 14 mg/1. A study of the effect of pH on the sorption of germanium showed that the greatest effect is attained in the range from 6.0 to 9.6. As the basicity increases, aluminum hydroxide begins to dissolve first. Thus, at pH = 9.6, about 20% aluminum is dissolved, while germanium remains in the precipitate. At pH = 11, about 70% aluminum and only 20% germanium are dissolved. At a ratio $Al_2O_3:GeO_2$ of less than 1, the sorption of germanium decreases sharply. Studies have shown that the sorption is chemical in character, i.e., is due to the formation of insoluble aluminum germanates.

A study of the coprecipitation of germanium, present in the ionic form, with ferric hydroxide at a concentration of Ge of about 1γ/ml, at pH = 8 and a ratio of Ge:Fe = 1:100 in the range of 20-80°C. showed that the process proceeds to the extent of 97-100%.[48] Such completeness is attained as early as the first two minutes of contact between the precipitate and the solution, and remains practically constant as the contact time increases to 24 hours. A study of the dependence of the coprecipitation of germanium on the

Fe:Ge ratio with values between 5 and 200 showed
that at ratios above 20, a complete coprecipitation
is achieved. The most complete process of
coprecipitation is observed at pH 6.0-9.5.

When the germanium content in the initial solution
is 108 mg/l and the ratio Ge:Fe = 1:39.4, the degree of coprecipitation of germanium with ferric
hydroxide exceeds 96% at a pH higher than 4. At
pH = 5.75, 99.7% germanium precipitates. As the
amount of iron in the initial solution decreases, the
degree of precipitation of germanium drops sharply,
and when the ratio Ge:Fe = 1:0.92 and pH = 7, only
66% germanium precipitates. This is evident from
Figures 17 and 18.

The influence of the duration of contact between
the solution and the precipitant was studied at the
ratio Ge:Fe = 1:1, pH = 7.5 and $20^{\circ}C$ in the range of
0.5-8.0 hr and a germanium concentration of 100
mg/l. The experiments showed that the degree of precipitation of germanium changes only in the range of

65.7-67.0%. Iron passes completely into the precipitate. This probably involves the coprecipitation
of iron germanates which are insoluble at pH 6.0-
9.5, not the adsorption of germanic acid by iron
hydroxide.

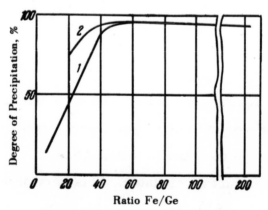

Fig. 17, Coprecipitation of Germanium Versus Amount of Iron
Hydroxide at pH 8, t = 70°C and
Ge Concentration of 1 v/mm.
1—Without Addition of $(NH_4)_2SO_4$
2—In a 2% Solution of $(NH_4)_2SO_4$

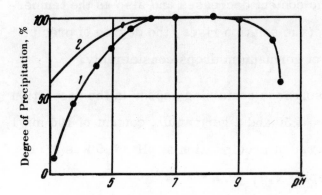

Fig. 18, Coprecipitation of Germanium and Iron Hydroxide Versus pH of the System (Concentration of Ge 1 v/ml, Ge:Fe = 1:100 t = 70°C).

1 — Germanium   2 — Iron Hydroxide

Similar results were obtained in a study of the precipitation of germanium from sulfate solutions containing zinc, copper and cadmium.[49]

Thus, for solutions containing zinc in the proportion Ge:Zn = 1:58.4 and a germanium concentration at the initial solution of 95 mg/l, the degree of precipitation at pH = 6.6 was 91.5% and at pH = 10.6, 97.0%. As

the zinc content decreases and also as the temperature of the solution rises, the degree of precipitation of germanium drops considerably.

For solutions containing copper in the proportion
Ge:Cu = 1:50 and a germanium content of 100 mg/l,
the degree of precipitation at pH = 7.5 was 97.1%,
and at pH = 8.7, 99.1%.

Upon precipitation from a solution containing
cadmium in the proportion Ge:Cd = 1:46.2 and a
germanium content of 92 mg/l, the degree of precipitation at pH = 5.7 was 93.6% and at pH = 10.1,
99.5%.

The precipitation of germanium from solutions
containing arsenate and silicate ions was carried
out.[49] The initial germanium content of the solution was 100 mg/l. Germanium did not precipitate
at all from solutions in which the ratio of germanium
to silica was 1:2, 1:5 and 1:10 in the range of
pH 3-10. From solutions with a germanium:silica
ratio of 1:70, the maximum quantity of precipitated

germanium at pH = 6.5-9.5 was 20-22%.

No precipitation of germanium was observed in the presence of arsenate ion in a solution with a weight ratio Ge:As = 1:2 and 1:246 in the range of pH 2-10.

The precipitation of germanium from sulfate solutions in the cases studied is due to the formation of chemical compounds between germanium and the elements present in the solution: zinc, copper, cadmium, and iron.[49]

3. BINARY AND TERNARY SYSTEMS OF GERMANIUM

Binary phase diagrams of the system formed by germanium with most metals, [1,3,50,51] many of which form germanides, have been investigated. Certain metals (silver, gold, zinc, cadmium, aluminum, the subgroup of gallium, germanium, and arsenic) form eutectic systems with germanium.

It may be assumed that in alkali metal germanides germanium is an anion.[3] Thus, when alkali metal

germanides react with inorganic acids, germanium
hydrides (polygermanes) are formed. The germanides and silicides of a whole series of metals
have been found to be isostructural.

The formation of chemical compounds between
germanium and metalloids is even more pronounced.
This indicates that metallic properties predominate
in germanium. [50]

Binary Systems of Germanium

Interaction of Germanium with Elements of Group I.
The interaction of germanium with all elements of
the alkali metal subgroup except francium has been
studied. [3,51] Compounds of type MeGe are thus
formed which can be obtained by direct synthesis.
They react with air and water. When heated in a
vacuum or in an inert atmosphere, they decompose
to form compounds of the type $MeGe_4$. The compounds $CsGe_4$, KGe_4, and $RbGe_4$ have been obtained.
Sodium germanide NaGe decomposes completely
when heated in a vacuum to $480^\circ C$.

Phase diagrams of the systems formed by germanium with elements of the copper subgroup have been studied fairly thoroughly. [3,51] Figure 19 shows the copper - germanium diagram. With copper, germanium yields the chemical compound Cu_3Ge, which forms by a peritectic reaction. There is a considerable region of solubility of germanium in copper (α- phase). The eutectic point is located at 36 at.% Ge. The melting point of the eutectic is $640^\circ C$. The solubility maximum of copper in germanium corresponds to $875^\circ C$ and amounts to less 3×10^{-4} at.% Cu.

The phase diagrams of germanium-silver and germanium-gold alloys belong to the eutectic type with narrow regions of homogeneity. [51] The eutectic point in the silver-germanium systems is located at 25.9 at.% Ge. The melting point of the eutectic is $651^\circ C$. The position of the eutectic point on the phase diagram of the gold-germanium system is displaced toward gold at 27 at.% Ge, and for this

FIGURE 19

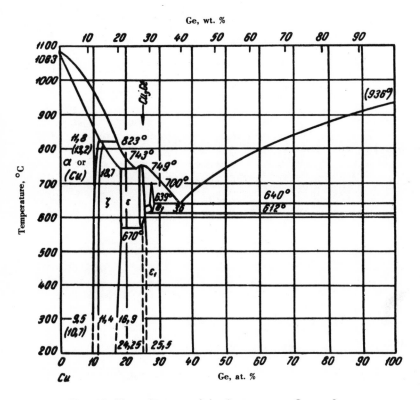

Fig. 19, Phase Diagram of the Germanium — Copper System.

reason a sharp drop in the melting point of gold is observed in the presence of relatively small amounts of germanium. The melting point of the eutectic is 350°C. There exist small regions of solid solutions of germanium in silver and gold.

Interaction of germanium with elements of group II.
The interaction of germanium with beryllium has not been sufficiently studied. It is known that the alloy with 10 wt.% germanium cooled from the melt has a two-phase structure with light-colored inclusions along the grain boundaries and inside the grains. [51]

The germanium - magnesium phase diagram (Figure 20[51]) shows only one chemical compound, Mg_2Ge, with a melting point of 1115°C and lattice parameter a = 6.390 ± 0.003Å. The solubility of germanium in magnesium at $400-600^{\circ}$C is less than 0.1 at.%.

Phase diagrams of systems formed by germanium with alkaline earth metals of the calcium subgroup have been the object of few studies. It has been noted

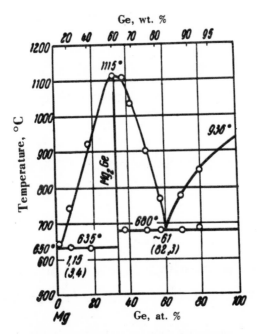

Fig. 20, Phase Diagram of the
Germanium - Magnesium System.

that chemical compounds are formed in these
systems.[3] The existence of several calcium germanides is known.[51] They are obtained by heating
mixtures of CaH_2 and Ge in a vacuum to 800-900°C.
Thus, CaGe has a rhombic lattice with parameters
$a = 4.001 \pm 0.001$ Å, b = 4.575 ± 0.002 Å and

c = 10.845 ± 0.001 Å. The compound Ca_2Ge also
has a rhombic lattice with parameters a = 9.069
± 0.0009 Å, b = 7.734 ± 0.0004 Å and c = 4.834
± 0.004 Å. Finally, the compound $CaGe_2$ has a
rhombohedral lattice with parameters a = 10.51 Å
and $\alpha = 21°41'$. The germanides Ca_2Ge and $CaGe_2$
decompose in moist air at $20°C$. When Ca_2Ge is
heated in air to $580-650°C$, oxidation takes place
with the formation of CaO and Ge. No data are
available in the literature on the interaction of germanium with radium.

The interaction of germanium with metals of
the zinc subgroup has been studied more
thoroughly.[1,50,51] With zinc and cadmium, germanium forms systems of simple eutectic type.
Figure 21 shows the zinc - germanium diagram.[51]
The eutectic point is located at 5.5 at.% germanium;
the melting point of the eutectic is $398°C$.

The thermodynamic properties of germanium-zinc
alloys were studied at $342-466°C$ thermogravi-

metrically (with continuous weighing) and an effusion chamber. [52] Despite the close values of the atomic radii of germanium and zinc, their mutual solubility in the solid state is very low. This is due to the dissimilar nature of the interatomic bonds: metallic type in zinc and covalent type in germanium. The penetration of germanium atoms into the zinc lattice is associated with a pronounced deformation, and hence with the absorption of energy. The entropy thereby increases. On the whole, a negative deviation of the system from the ideal state is obtained. A similar deviation also takes place in the liquid state.

On the cadmium - germanium diagram, the eutectic point is located at 2.9 at.% germanium, and the melting point of the eutectic is $319^{\circ}C$.

The solubility of germanium in liquid mercury is very low and becomes appreciable only above $250^{\circ}C$. [50,51] At $300^{\circ}C$, up to 0.027 wt.% germanium dissolves in mercury.

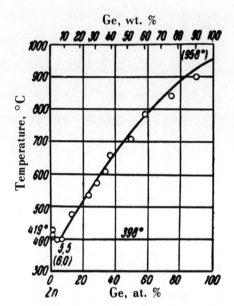

Fig. 21, Phase Diagram of the
System Germanium - Zinc.

Interaction of Germanium with Elements of Group

III. Data on the interaction of germanium with

scandium and yttrium are not available in the

literature. The existence of chemical compounds of

germanium with lanthanides and actinides is known.[51]

The compound $PrGe_2$ has a tetragonal structure with

12 atoms in the unit cell; the lattice parameters
$a = 4.253$ Å, $b = 13.940$ Å, $c/a = 3.277$. In the
system germanium - plutonium, the existence of the
following phases is known: Pu_2Ge_3 with a distorted
lattice of the type of $Al B_2$, $PuGe_2$ with a tetragonal
structure, and $PuGe_3$ with a cubic structure, in
which the lattice parameter $a = 4.223$ Å.

The system germanium - uranium contains the
compounds U_5Ge_3, U_3Ge_4, UGe_2 and UGe_3.[54] The
compound UGe_3 has a Cu_3Au-type structure and
lattice parameter $a = 4.206$ Å.[51]

No data are available on the interaction of germanium with boron. With aluminum and rare metals
of the thallium subgroup, germanium forms systems
of eutectic type.

In the aluminum - germanium system, the eutectic
alloy contains 30.3 at.% germanium and has a melting point of $424^{\circ}C$. The solubility of germanium in
aluminum in the solid state at $424^{\circ}C$ does not
exceed 2.8 at.%.[51]

X-ray structural analysis of gallium-germanium alloys has shown the absence of any new phases. [55] Some slight changes in the parameters of the germanium crystal lattice occur when up to 1% gallium is dissolved therein. The phase diagram is shown in Fig. 22. A pseudoeutectic system is formed when up to 2.1% gallium dissolves in solid germanium (at 30°C). The microhardness of the eutectic is 35-59 kg/mm^2. [56] The electrical resistivity of gallium is 60×10^{-6} ohm cm: it increases to 2.1×10^{-3} ohm cm when the germanium content is 2.5%.

The thallium - germanium diagram is of pseudo-eutectic type. The pseudoeutectic point is displayed toward the melting point of thallium. [56] The addition of thallium to germanium (up to 85%) lowers the melting point of the alloy to 800°C. The hardness of thallium is 3 kg/mm^2, but the hardness of the alloys increases to 9 kg/mm^2 when the germanium content is 50%. All the alloys display a metallic conduction.

The indium - germanium diagram, [51] in which the pseudoeutectic point is practically located on the side of indium, is similar.

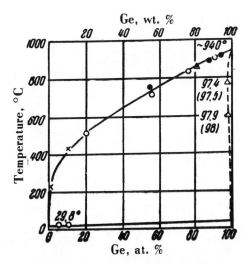

**Fig. 22, Phase Diagram of The
System Germanium - Gallium.**

Interaction of Germanium with Elements of Group

IV. Germanium forms chemical compounds with

elements of the titanium subgroup. Thus, the

existence of the following compounds has been

established in the titanium - germanium system:

Ti_5Ge_3 with the structural type of Mn_5Si_3 and lattice

parameters a = 7.552 Å, b = 5.234 Å; $TiGe_2$ with the

structural type of $TiSi_2$ and lattice parameters

a = 8.594 Å, b = 5.030 Å, c = 8.864 Å, and

TiGe.[51, 57] At 500°C, the solubility of germanium

in α-titanium is close to 2 at.%. The eutectic of

β-titanium and of the compound Ti_5Ge_3 corresponds

to a content of 16 at.% germanium and has a melting

point of 1410°C. A decrease in the stability of the

bond is parallel to the increase in interatomic

distances: TiGe (d = 2.42 Å), Ti_5Ge_3 (d = 2.62 Å)

and $TiGe_2$ (d = 2.64 Å).[58]

The maximum solubility of germanium in zirconium

in the solid state is 0.5-1.0 wt.%.[51] The compound

Zr_5Ge_3 has a melting point of 2330°C, and its lattice

parameters are a = 7.99 Å, c = 5.54 Å. At 2240°C,

the compound ZrGe is formed by a peritectic re-

action. In addition, the existence of the compound

$ZrGe_2$ with lattice parameters a = 3.7892 Å, b =

14.975 Å and c = 3.7606 Å was noted.

In the system germanium - hafnium, the compound

$HfGe_2$ was identified; it had a rhombic structure

with lattice parameters a = 3.8154 Å, b = 15.004 Å,

and c = 3.7798 Å.

Germanium does not react with carbon. However, the formation of carbides of certain metals was observed at the phase boundary between liquid germanium and graphite, for example, those of tantalum or tungsten if they were present in the melt.[59]

Germanium and silicon are infinitely soluble in each other in the liquid and solid state. Both elements have the same type of crystal lattice, similar atomic sizes, and occupy adjacent positions in the electromotive series. The phase diagram of the germanium - silicon system is shown in Figure 23.[51, 60] The phenomenon of intracrystalline liquation is pronounced in the alloys of this system, since the interdiffusion in the solid state is extremely slight. Therefore, it is difficult to obtain a homogeneous alloy of germanium and silicon even in a polycrystalline form, let alone in the form of a single crystal. When alloys of various compositions containing germanium in amounts of 14 to 84% are

obtained, a compositional inhomogeneity in the range
of 2-16% is observed.

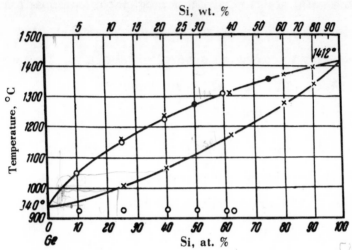

Fig. 23, Phase Diagram of The System Germanium - Silicon.
O – Cooling   X – Heating

Experiments have shown that the zone melting of
powdered-metal (premelted) blanks makes it possible
to obtain a homogeneous solid solution of silicon in
germanium with a content of 2.25 to 40% of silicon
in the form of a polycrystalline ingot.   The displacement rate of the zone should be no more than 5-7
mm/hr. However, as was shown by x-ray diffraction

patterns, such an alloy has an inhomogeneous composition. In order to extend the length of the region
of the solid solution with a homogeneous composition
and enlarge the grains of the alloy to 4-6 mm, it is
necessary to carry out several passes of the zone at
the above-indicated rate, each time changing the
direction of its travel.

The phase diagrams of the systems germanium -
tin and germanium - lead are eutectic in character.[50,51] The eutectic point lies practically on
the side of tin and lead. For the system germanium -
tin, it was established that the mutual solubility of
the components in the solid state does not exceed
0.6 at.% Ge and 1.0 at.% Sn, respectively.

Interaction of Germanium with Elements of
Group V. Germanium forms chemical compounds
with metals of the vanadium subgroup. The
existence of the compound V_3Ge with a β-W-type
cubic structure and lattice constant a = 4.769 Å was
established in the germanium - vanadium system.[51]

The interaction of germanium with niobium is associated with the formation of several chemical compounds. [51] X-ray structural studies established the cubic structure of Nb_3Ge (a = 5.168 Å). The structure of Nb_3Ge_2 is of the same type as that of $CrSi_2$, and has lattice parameters a = 4.966 Å and c = 6.781 Å. In addition, the phases Nb_3Ge_2 and Nb_2Ge were detected. The former and the two latter phases are stable at least up to $1650°C$.

The compounds Ta_5Ge, Ta_2Ge, and $TaGe_2$ were found in the germanium - tantalum system. [51] $TaGe_2$ has a $CrSi_2$ - type cubic lattice with parameters a = 4.958 Å and c = 6.751 Å. At $1280°C$, this compound decomposes to form Ta_2Ge and a liquid phase rich in germanium.

With nitrogen, germanium forms the compound Ge_3N_2 and Ge_3N_4. GeNH and $Ge(NH)_2$ are also known. [1, 51] The nitride Ge_3N_2 is formed when germanium dioxide is treated in a stream of ammonia up to $750°C$ [61] or when germanium metal is heated in a stream of nitrogen up to 850-900°C. [51] The nitride Ge_3N_2 has an orthorhombic structure with lattice parameters a = 3.88 Å, b = 7.10 Å and c = 5.94 Å. The other nitride, Ge_3N_4, can be obtained by heating metallic germanium in a stream of ammonia up to 750°C. [61] It has a rhombohedral structure with parameter c = 8.62 Å and α = 108°.

There is evidence to indicate the volatility of germanium in a stream of nitrogen at 800-850°C. A nitrogen content up to 5% was detected in the sublimates, indicating a volatilization of the nitrogen compounds of germanium. [19]

Germanium forms the compound GeP with phosphorus. [1]

The interaction of germanium with arsenic forms the chemical compound GeAs and $GeAs_2$. [50,51] GeAs has the following lattice parameters: a = 3.721 Å, b = 10.12 Å, and c = 14.74 Å. The parameters of the other compound are as follows: a = 22.84 Å, b = 378 A, c = 9.45 Å, and β = 43.97°.

The phase diagram of the system germanium -
arsenic (Figure 24) indicates an appreciable mutual
solubility of germanium and arsenic.[51] The melting points of the compounds are close to each other
(732°C for GeAs$_2$ and 737°C for GeAs).

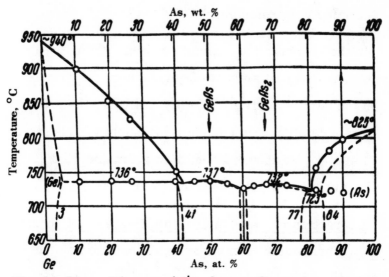

Fig. 24, Phase Diagram of the System Germanium - Arsenic.

Germanium forms eutectic alloys with antimony
and bismuth. In the germanium - antimony system,
the eutectic point is located at 17 at.% germanium,

and the melting point of the eutectic is 592°C. [50]
Qualitative x-ray analysis and measurement of the
magnetic susceptibility of samples subjected to
heating at 540°C for 4 months have shown that the
solubility in the solid state at this temperature is
about 2.5 at.% germanium in antimony and 2.4 at.%
antimony in germanium. [51]

In the germanium - bismuth system, the eutectic
contains a small amount of germanium. [51] Based
on the data of qualitative x-ray analysis, the solid-
state solubility of germanium in bismuth is about
1.5 at.%, and that of bismuth in germanium, 2 at.%
after holding for several months at 250°C.

Interaction of Germanium with Elements of Group
VI. Germanium forms chemical compounds with
metals of the chromium subgroup. [3]

In the germanium - chromium system, the existence of three compounds has been noted: Cr_3Ge has
a β-W-type lattice with parameter a = 4.623 $\overset{\circ}{A}$, and
Cr_3Ge_2 and CrGe have an FeSi-type-lattice with

parameter a = 4.789 Å. [51] All three compounds are
isostructural with the corresponding silicon compounds. It was found that certain alloys in this
system in the range of 50 to 98 at.% germanium are
ferromagnetic. The ferromagnetism of these alloys
is probably due to the existence of a single ferromagnetic phase, $CrGe_3$. [62]

X-ray structural studies of sintered mixtures of
molybdenum and germanium powders established the
following phases: Mo_3Ge, Mo_3Ge_2, Mo_2Ge_3 and
$MoGe_2$. [51] The latter compound has two modifications. The high-temperature modification $MoGe_2$
has a tetragonal lattice with six atoms in the unit cell
and lattice parameters a = 3.313 Å and c = 8.195 Å.
The melting point of Mo_3Ge is above 1750°C.

Germanium forms a whole series of compounds with
oxygen and sulfur. These systems will be examined
below.

The interaction of germanium with selenium and
tellurium also involves the formation of chemical

compounds: GeSe, $GeSe_2$ and GeTe. [1, 50]   A phase
diagram of the germanium - tellurium system is
shown in Figure 25. GeTe melts at 725°C. This
compound has two modifications. The low-temper-
ature modification has a distorted sodium chloride
structure with lattice constant a = 5.976 $\overset{o}{A}$ and
$\alpha = 88.35^\circ$; the high-temperature modification has a
face-centered cubic structure. [51, 63]

Germanium selenides were synthesized by vacuum
melting in quartz ampules at 10^{-2}-10^{-3} mm Hg,
900°C, [64] and soaking for 5 hr at this temperature.
Variable-composition selenides $GeSe_x$ were obtained,
where x varies from 3 to 24. A study of the electrical conductivity of germanium selenides showed
that the atomic bonds are covalent in character. The
melting point of GeSe is 667°C.

Interaction of Germanium with Elements of Group
VII. The interaction of germanium with manganese
and rhenium was studied in the manganese subgroup. [50, 51] The phase diagram of the germanium -

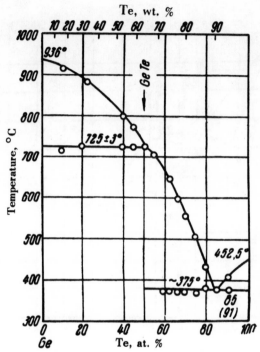

Fig. 25, Phase Diagram of the
System Germanium - Tellurium.

manganese system is illustrated in Figure 26. The

following compounds are formed: $Mn_{3.25}Ge$,

Mn_5Ge_3, and Mn_3Ge_2. There is a sizable solid

solution region on the side of manganese up to 10

at. %.

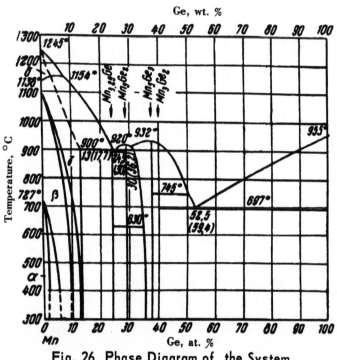

**Fig. 26, Phase Diagram of the System
Germanium - Magnesium**

In Mn-Ge alloys containing from 40 to 95% germanium, there is a single ferromagnetic phase
Mn_3Ge_2. The values of the resistivity
$(\rho \approx 10^{-3}$ ohm cm) and magnetic moment (M = 2.5
μ B) indicate the presence of metallic-type bonding
in this compound.[65]

Germanium displays a pronounced tendency to form chemical compounds with hydrogen, fluorine, chlorine, bromine and iodine. [1, 50] These compounds will be considered individually.

Interaction of Germanium with Elements of Group VIII. The literature contains data on the interaction of germanium with all metals of group VIII. [50, 51] This interaction is characterized by an exceptional abundance of chemical compounds, large regions of solid solutions, and transformations in the solid state.

The system germanium - iron, whose phase diagram is shown in Figure 27, has two chemical compounds: Fe_2Ge and $FeGe_2$. Up to 20 at.%, germanium can dissolve in iron. The maximum solubility of iron in germanium at 750-940°C varies between 5×10^{14} and 1.5×10^{15} atoms/cm^3. [66] In this temperature range, the diffusion coefficient increases from 1.06×10^{-6} to 4.3×10^{-6} cm/sec, changing in accordance with the law $D = 0.13 \, e^{-E/RT}$

where E = 25000 cal/mole   or 1.1 eV is the activation energy of the diffusion.

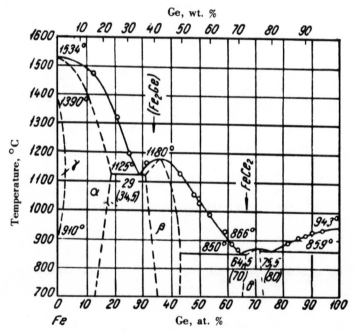

Fig. 27, Phase Diagram of the System Germanium - Iron.

The high rate and low activation energy of the diffusion leads to the assumption that iron diffuses along the interstices in the germanium lattice, as do copper, nickel, and lithium. The eutectic of $FeGe_2$ and germanium is unstable and undergoes a transformation at $830^{o}C$.

For other systems, the existence of the following phases has been established: Co_2Ge, $CoGe$, Co_2Ge_3, $CoGe_2$, $IrGe$, Ir_3Ge_7, Ir_3Ge_4, Ir_4Ge_5, Pd_5Ge_2, Pd_4Ge, Pd_2Ge, $PdGe$, Ni_2Ge, Ni_3Ge, $NiGe$, $CsGe_2$, Pt_2Ge, $PtGe$, Pt_3Ge, Pt_3Ge_2, $PtGe_2$, Pt_2Ge_3, $RuGe_4$, Rh_2Ge, Rh_5Ge_3, $RhGe$. [50, 51, 67]

Ternary Systems Involving Germanium

Data on ternary systems involving germanium are scarce.

A study of the Sn - Ge - Te system has shown that a continuous series of solid solutions with a minimum on the solid-liquid diagram is formed between the two nonisostructural compounds SnTe and GeTe. [63] The face-centered cubic lattice of the compound SnTe gradually changes into the face-centered rhombohedral lattice of the compound GeTe.

Isothermal reactions at 500°C in the nickel - copper - germanium system were studied by the x-ray and metallographic methods. [68] $Ni_3Cu_2Ge_2$ has a hexagonal structure, $Ni_{15}Cu_{65}Ge_{20}$ has an A13-type structure, and $Ni_{15}Cu_{58}Ge_{22}$ has a structure analogous to γ- bronze.

Homogeneous alloys were found in the copper - germanium - silicon system (Table 13). [69]

Table 13, Lattice Parameters of
Face-Centered Cubic ∝ Alloys.

Composition, at. %			Lattice
Cu	Si	Ge	Parameters, $\overset{\circ}{A}$
90,0	7,5	2,5	3,6275
90,0	5,0	5,0	3,6347
90,0	2,5	7,5	3,6420

The ternary system copper - zinc - germanium was studied. [70] A simple two-phase equilibrium exists between the σ phase of the copper - germanium system and β and β' phases of the copper -

zinc system. Both phases have sizable homogeneous intervals in the ternary system. The hexagonal σ phase is capable of dissolving up to 21 at.% Zn and up to 10 at.% Ge. The cubic β phase can dissolve up to 7.5 at.% Ge.

Carbides of the type T_3BC_x, where T stands for the metals nickel, cobalt, iron, manganese, and B for the elements germanium, indium, zinc, tin, etc., form a special group of carbides. They have a face-centered cubic lattice in which the B - atoms occupy the corners of the cube and the T - atoms the centers of the lateral faces. [71]

A phase was obtained containing 72.7 at.% Ni, 24.2% Ge, and 3.1% C, with a face-centered cubic lattice (parameter a = 3.57 Å). The phase was not ferromagnetic.

A phase of the composition $Co_3GeC_{0.25}$, also non-ferromagnetic, was found in cobalt germanium carbide.

From the phase diagram of the iron - germanium
system it follows that mixed crystals of iron and
germanium are in equilibrium with the hexagonal
phase Fe_2Ge. In the alloy (70.0 at.% Fe, 23.0% Ge,
and 7.0% C), a ternary carbide with a face-centered
cubic lattice was identified. The faint lines of fer-
rite and of the binary phase Fe_2Ge represent a substructure with lattice constant a = 3.65 Å. The
lattice parameter of the ternary carbide is also
equal to 3.65 Å for alloys with three phases: mixed
iron crystals, ternary carbide with a substructure,
and graphite (for example, 76.0 at.% Fe, 16.6% Ge
and 7.4% C). Apparently, in this case the region of
homogeneity of the carbide in equilibrium with iron
is very small. The limit of saturation of the carbide by carbon calculated from the two-phase alloy
is 9 at.%, which corresponds to the formula
$Fe_3GeC_{0.4}$. This formula is inaccurate because of
the formation of mixed crystals of iron with germanium. Measurements of the line intensities   of

the x-ray diffraction patterns made it possible to determine the content of carbon in the carbide and to derive a more precise formula: $Fe_3GeC_{0.45}$.

The ternary carbide is ferromagnetic. The Curie point of the ternary compound is $395^{\circ}C$.

The phase $Mn_{3.25}Ge$ is known in the manganese - germanium - carbon system. In alloys containing 70.0-75.0 at.% Mn, 10.0-13.3% Ge and 14.3-16.7%C, a ternary carbide was found with lattice parameter a = 3.86-3.87 $\overset{\circ}{A}$. The carbide is strongly ferromagnetic, and its Curie point is $330^{\circ}C$.

Compounds of the type MeMnGe, where Me is cobalt and nickel, are known in the manganese - cobalt - germanium and manganese - nickel - germanium systems. X-ray structural studies of alloys of Me_2MnGe-type have been made.[72] In the first system, this alloy is homogeneous and is a ternary compound. The alloy Ni_2MnGe is inhomogeneous; apparently, the composition of the compound deviates from this formula.

The following compounds were obtained in the germanium - zinc - phosphorus and germanium - zinc - arsenic systems. [73] $ZnGeP_2$ with lattice parameters a = 5.46 Å and c/a = 1.97; $ZnGeAs_2$ with lattice parameters a = 5.67 Å and c/a = 1.967.

Only one phase of the composition $CdGeAs_2$ (a = 5.949 Å and c/a = 1.889) is known in the germanium - cadmium - arsenic system.

4. GERMANIUM OXIDES

Figure 28 shows a phase diagram of the germanium - oxygen system. [74] Two oxides of germanium exist: the monoxide and the dioxide. As is evident from the diagram, solid germanium can dissolve substantial amounts of oxygen, up to 60 at.%.

As the oxygen concentration in germanium increases, the lattice of germanium expands slightly at first, then contracts. This is obvious from measurements of the lattice parameter of germanium made as the oxygen content increased: [75]

Atomic ratio Ge : 0 . 1 : 0.000 1 : 0.2575 1 : 0.495

$a_o \pm 0.0004 \overset{o}{A}$...... 5.6447   5.6454   5.6461

Atomic ratio Ge : 0 . 1 : 0.810 1 : 1.020 1 : 1.320

$a_o \pm 0.0004 \overset{o}{A}$...... 5.6466   5.6461   5.6455

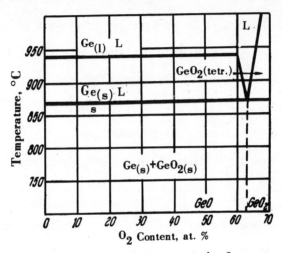

Fig. 28, Phase Diagram of the System
Germanium - Oxygen.

At temperatures above the melting point of germanium and at a germanium:oxygen ratio of 1:1, the
lines of germanium disappear from the x-ray patterns, although the sample still remains solid. This
is caused by a disordering of the germanium lattice

due to an interchange of the sites of germanium and oxygen atoms. [75]

Germanium Monoxide

The existence of this compound was first indicated by K. Winkler, but he was unable to isolate it in the pure form. [76] Germanium monoxide hydrate is obtained by reducing a solution of germanium dioxide (0.25-0.50 M) in a 6 N hydrochloric acid solution with excess 30% hypophosphoric acid followed by neutralization of the solution with dilute ammonia. [76]

Moist germanous hydroxide readily oxidizes in air, so that the precipitation and washing should be carried out in an atmosphere of an inert gas. The hydroxide prepared in this manner is a yellow or red gelatinous substance. If the precipitation is made from a boiling solution, the product obtained is dark brown and somewhat more granular. A white precipitate of germanous hydroxide forms when a concentrated solution of germanium dioxide

(1.5-2.0 M) in hydrochloric acid is reduced with excess hypophosphoric acid, and the hydrolysis is carried out by dilution with water. [77] In contact with the solution, this white form of germanous hydroxide gradually changes into the usual red modification. The white modification is more soluble in hydrochloric acid than the colored forms. Germanous hydroxide is obtained from solutions of 25% sulfuric acid by reducing tetravalent germanium to the divalent state with zinc. [4] Any other strong reductant may be used for this reaction. Being amphoteric, germanous hydroxide displays the properties of a weak acid. In addition to its appreciable solubility in hydrochloric and other halogen acids, some solubility is also observed in alkalis. [4]

The solubility of germanous hydroxide of divalent germanium in water and hydrochloric acid was studied at 25° C. [78] In water it is $2 \pm 1 \times 10^{-4}$ mole/l. In a 4 M solution of hydrochloric acid, the solubility is less than 0.01 mole/l, but it increases quickly in

more concentrated solutions. The earlier value of
the solubility of germanous hydroxide in water (5 x
10^{-3} mole/1)[77] may have been high because of
experimental errors.

Germanous hydroxide dehydrates completely on
heating in a nitrogen atmosphere to 650°C. A black
substance is formed whose chemical composition is
that of the monoxide. It can be analyzed by oxidation with hydrogen peroxide to germanium dioxide.
Anhydrous germanium monoxide does not react
with atmospheric moisture or oxygen at room
temperature. It is very slightly affected by hydrochloric and sulfuric acid and by solutions of strong
alkalis. It is slowly oxidized by vapors of strong
nitric acid, potassium permanganate, and chlorine
water, but quickly oxidized by hydrogen peroxide
in the presence of ammonia.[76]

The yellow form of germanous hydroxide is thermodynamically   unstable and converts into the brown
form. This transformation was studied quantita-

tively in the system GeO (yellow) - GeO_2 - 0.0025 N
HCl - GeO (brown). [78] The concentration of
hydrochloric acid was relatively low, so that the reaction went fairly slowly. Two electrodes, made
from a spiral of a noble metal, were coated with a
paste of GeO and GeO_2. The potential of the cell
was 0.155 V, which corresponded to a free energy
change ΔF^o = 7200 cal/mole for the two-electron
reaction GeO (yellow) $\longrightarrow$ GeO (brown).

As expected, the potential of the cell decreased
gradually with time owing to the spontaneous transformation of the yellow monoxide to the brown
monoxide.

The oxidation of germanium monoxide in air begins
at 550^oC. If germanium monoxide is heated in a
stream of nitrogen, it sublimes above 710^oC. [76]
When germanium monoxide is heated in a stream of
nitrogen in a platinum or nickel boat above 550^oC,
the dioxide and free germanium are formed, the
latter forming an alloy with the metal of the boat.

On heating in a quartz boat, the monoxide reacts with silica above 800°C to give a yellow glass.

When germanium monoxide is acted upon by hydrogen chloride at 175°C, trichlorogermane and water are formed. Chlorine interacts with the monoxide at 250°C, forming germanium dioxide and germanium tetrachloride. The reaction with bromine is similar.[76]

The problems of formation and volatilization of germanium monoxide at high temperatures have been treated most thoroughly in refs.[75, 80 and 81] Gaseous germanium monoxide can be obtained by reacting metallic germanium with its dioxide at temperatures above 600°C according to the reaction

$$Ge \text{ (s)} + GeO_2 \text{ (s)} \longrightarrow 2GeO \text{ (g)}$$

This reaction also occurs at temperatures above 800°C as a result of the reaction of metallic germanium with carbon dioxide,[20] or with nitrogen containing about 1% oxygen,[19] or else with oxygen at low pressures.[16-18] Finally, the reduction of germanium dioxide by carbon monoxide at temperatures around 1000°C also produces GeO (g).[21, 82, 83] The rate of this process has been studied[87] (Figure 29). In the case of the reduction of germanium dioxide by hydrogen, the process is carried out at 600-650°C in order to reduce the losses of germanium in the form of monoxide.[84, 85] If the reduction is conducted at a higher temperature, a vigorous formation and volatilization of germanium monoxide take place. After leaving the high-temperature zone, the gaseous monoxide either condenses virtually without any decomposition (in a condenser) or decomposes to form germanium and germanium dioxide. The condensed germanium dioxide is highly amorphous and does not produce any lines on x-ray diffraction patterns. In the case of condensation without a condenser and at fairly high temperatures, the rate of the disproportionation reaction of gaseous germanium monoxide is higher than the rate of condensation,

and the x-ray patterns of the solid product show
lines of free germanium and its dioxide.

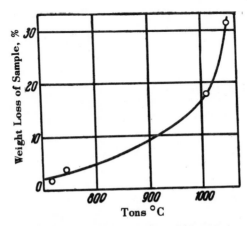

Fig. 29, Weight Loss of Sample
Versus Temperature During Reduction of Germanium Dioxide
by Carbon Dioxide.

The reaction of germanium with its dioxide begins
at $600^{o}C$, proceeds at an appreciable rate at $700^{o}C$,
but is rapid at $1000^{o}C$. [20, 86] The process is carried out in a vacuum or in an inert atmosphere, and
the sublimate formed deposits in a condenser. A
brownish-red substance (light yellow in a thin layer)
is thus formed. The density of germanium monoxide

determined pycnometrically in carbon tetrachloride is equal to 4.40 g/cm^3. The substance is highly amorphous, does not dissolve in water, but can form aqueous colloidal solutions which are red in color.

The results of a study of the rate of reaction between germanium and carbon by means of the gas stream method are illustrated graphically in Figure 30. The reaction rate increased abruptly above 800°C. The germanium monoxide thus formed collected in the condenser. The sublimate obtained at 700°C was light-yellow in color. As the reaction temperature rose, the color of the condensate changed from brown to dark-brown. The product which deposited at lower temperatures was an extremely fine powder; the sublimate obtained at high temperatures was vitreous and harder (Mohs hardness 5). All the sublimates investigated had an amorphous structure. However, the x-ray patterns of certain products showed the lines of germanium

dioxide and germanium. This was due to the disproportionation reaction

$$2GeO \ (g) \ \rightleftharpoons \ GeO_2 + Ge.$$

The gas stream method was used to study the reaction of formation of germanium monoxide in the
course of oxidation of the metal in air at low pressure (34 and 4 mm Hg).[86] The vaporization of
germanium began as low as $600^{o}C$ and increased
substantially with the temperature (Figure 31). The

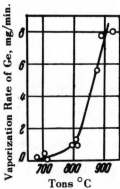

formation of germanium
monoxide due to oxida-
tion in a stream of air
at low pressure was
more extensive than in
the reaction of german -
ium with carbon dioxide.
Germanium monoxide
collected in the con-
denser in the form of a
dense, vitreous mass.

Fig. 30, Temperature
Dependence of the
Vaporization Rate of
Germanium in a Stream
of Carbon Dioxide at
Atmospheric Pressure.

The sublimate is brittle and its color changes from brown to dark brown as the reaction temperature rises. According to the x-ray structural data, the sublimate is also amorphous. As was shown by chemical analyses, the stoichiometric ratio of germanium to oxygen corresponding to the formula GeO is closer the higher the temperature of the reaction and the lower the air pressure, i.e., the concentration of oxygen in the space occupied by the gas. At reaction temperatures above the melting point of germanium, the rate of formation and volatilization of germanium monoxide decreases sharply. This is due to an appreciable decrease in the surface of the interface.

For every temperature there is an optimum oxygen concentration at which the oxidation rate of germanium does not surpass the sublimation rate of the monoxide being formed. Otherwise, a layer of dioxide forms on the surface of the germanium, and the process virtually comes to a halt.

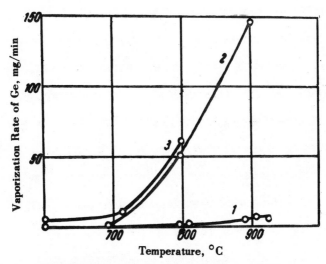

Fig. 31. Temperature Dependence of The Vaporization Rate of Germanium.

1—In a Stream of Carbon Dioxide; 2—In a Stream of Air at a Pressure of 34 mm Hg; 3—Same, at 4 mm Hg;

The vapor pressure of germanium monoxide was measured by several different methods. Ref. [81] gives results obtained by a dynamic method (in a gas stream) and a static method, whereas the results of ref. [80] were obtained by the effusion method.

Experiments involving x-ray diffraction studies of the solid residues have shown that solid germanium monoxide at 600°C decomposes in the course of

several hours, but at 700°C, in a few minutes. For
this reason, in measurements made by the gas
stream method, what was studied was not the
equilibrium pressure over germanium monoxide,
but actually that over a mixture of germanium and
its dioxide. The vapor pressure of germanium
monoxide was calculated by assuming a unimole-
cular composition of the vapor. Table 14 shows
the results of the measurement of the vapor pressure of germanium monoxide by the gas stream
method. [81]

Assuming that the decomposition rate of germanium
monoxide is low in the range of $600-700^{\circ}$, the
equilibrium pressures were measured by the static
method. This method made it possible to determine
the equilibrium pressure both over germanium
monoxide, when the measurements were conducted
at temperatures below 700°C, and over the decomposed product (at higher temperatures).

Table 14, Vapor Pressure of Germanium Monoxide Obtained by Gas Stream Method.

Temperature °C	Flow Rate Of Nitrogen ml/min	Duration, min	Amount Of Condensate mg	Pressure, mm Hg	
				In The System	GeO
707	39,9	150	11,34	740	0,355
	30,4	142	9,20	739	0,399
	25,0	165	10,28	739	0,465
	11,6	200	6,87	740	0,555
	0,0	—	—	—	0,683 ± 0,1
808	44,2	69	107,4	753	6,65
	36,4	120	166,9	752	7,20
	27,3	23	24,3	750	7,28
	18,3	108	92,0	751	8,75
	0,0	—	—	—	9,48 ± 0,3

The vapor pressure of germanium monoxide obtained by the static method is as follows:[81]

Temp. $^\circ$C	642	644	675	705	754
P_{GeO}, mm Hg.	1.80	3.29	9.90	28.48	1.79
Temp. $^\circ$C	765	769	784	811	850
P_{GeO}, mm Hg.	1.80	3.29	5.26	9.90	28.48

As is evident from the above data, an abrupt change in the vapor pressure of germanium monoxide takes place at temperatures above 705°C. This is due to the fact that at high temperatures the solid phase is not the monoxide but a mixture of germanium and its dioxide.

The results obtained by the dynamic and static methods are shown graphically in Fure 32. The values of the vapor pressure of germanium monoxide form a straight line. This supports the assumption that only monomeric molecules of germanium monoxide are present in the vapor. Curve 2 of Figure 32 is described by the equation:

$$\log P \text{ (mm Hg)} = -\frac{13750}{T} + 15.464,$$

whence the temperature dependence of the free

energy of sublimation of germanium monoxide is

$$\Delta F_T = 63000 - 57.9\,T.$$

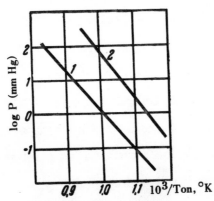

Fig. 32, Temperature
Dependence of the
Vapor Pressure of
Germanium Monoxide.
1—Pressure Over Mixture
Ge+Ge O_2 ; 2—Pressure
Over GeO;

The change in enthalpy and entropy on sublimation

of the monoxide in the range of 640-705°C is then

$$\Delta H_T = 63.0 \text{ kcal/mole, and}$$
$$\Delta S_T = 57.9 \text{ cal/mole deg.}$$

Curve 1 of Figure 32 is described by the equation

$$\log P \text{ (mm Hg)} = -\frac{12000}{T} + 12.05,$$

which corresponds to the equilibrium pressure over a mixture of germanium and its dioxide. The changes in the enthalpy and entropy of this process are:

$$\Delta H_T = 54.8 \text{ kcal/mole, and}$$
$$\Delta S_T = 42.0 \text{ cal/mole deg.}$$

Knudsen's effusion method was used to measure the vapor pressure of germanium monoxide at $485-586^{\circ}C$. [80] The data obtained are shown in Table 15.

The average value ($\Delta H_O = 55.1$ kcal/mole) is in satisfactory agreement with the values calculated from the data of ref. [81] On the basis of the experiments, the following thermodynamic characteristics of the sublimation of germanium dioxide were obtained:

$$\Delta F_T = 54600 + 6.9\, T \log T - 62\, T \text{ cal/mole};$$

$$\Delta H_T = 54600 - 3\, T \text{ cal/mole};$$

$$\Delta S_T = 59 - 6.9 \log T \text{ cal/mole deg}.$$

At $298\degree K$,

$$\Delta H_{298} = 53.7 \pm 1.0 \text{ kcal/mole}.$$

For the dissociation of GeO (g), $\Delta H_{298} = 159$ kcal/mole (calculated by linear extrapolation in a homologous series), so that if other thermodynamic data are available, one can carry out the following thermochemical calculation:

$$Ge\ (g) + 1/2\ O_2\ (g) \rightarrow GeO\ (g) \qquad -159.0$$

$$Ge\ (s) \rightarrow Ge\ (g) \qquad 85.2$$

$$+$$

$$1/2\ O_2\ (d) \rightarrow O\ (g) \qquad 59.2$$

$$1/2 GeO_2\ (s) \rightarrow 1/2 Ge\ (s) + 1/2\ O_2\ (g)\ 64.2$$

$1/2 Ge\ (s) + 1/2 GeO_2\ (s) \rightarrow GeO\ (g)\ 50.0$ kcal/mole, the result of which ($\Delta H_{298} = 50$ kcal/mole) shows that the experimental and calculated values are close.

The heat of formation of solid germanium monoxide was determined calorimetrically.[81] The value of -77.2 kcal/mole was thus obtained, which corresponds to the standard heat of formation of solid germanium monoxide according to the reaction

$$Ge + 1/2O_2 \longrightarrow GeO \text{ (s)}.$$

The heat of formation of gaseous germanium monoxide based on various data is shown in Table 16. In the calculations, use may be made of the average value $\Delta H_{298} = 12 \pm 4$ kcal/mole.

The entropy of gaseous germanium monoxide under standard conditions is taken as 56.1 cal/mole deg[81] or 52.6 cal/mole deg. [7]

Finally, the heat capacity of gaseous germanium monoxide is close to 7 cal/mole deg;[81] it may be assumed to be equal to 7.39 cal/mole deg at 25°C. [7]

No data are available in the literature on the fusion of germanium monoxide. Its sublimation temperature at a vapor pressure of 760 mm Hg is 815°C.[81]

Table 15, Vapor Pressures of Germanium Monoxide and Enthalpy Changes On Sublimation.

Temperature °C	$P_{GeO} \cdot 10^3$ mm Hg	H_O, kcal/mole	Temperature °C	$P_{GeO} \cdot 10^3$ mm Hg	H_O, kcal/mole
485	$5,10 \cdot 10^{-2}$	56,790	543	1,14	55,930
497	0,99	53,160	543	1,97	55,030
515	1,37	53,790	562	8,05	55,030
517	0,28	56,440	586	5,85	55,960

Table 16, Heat of Formation

Temperature, °C	Heat Of Formation kcal/mole	Literature Source	Temperature, °C	Heat Of Formation kcal/mole	Literature Source
800	−8,4	[81]	25	−6,0±4,0	[78, 88]
25	−10,8±4,0	[80]	25	−22,8	[7]

This indicates a high degree of volatility of germanium monoxide at the temperatures of pyrometallurgical processes.

Germanium Dioxide

Germanium dioxide may be obtained by hydrolyzing germanium tetrahalides or alkali metal germanates. The deposits thus formed are so thin that their crystalline structure is difficult to establish even with a microscope. [89]

X-ray diffraction analysis of these products has shown a crystal structure analogous to that of quartz and belonging to the hexagonal type. If the hydrolysis product is subjected to calcination at $380^{\circ}C$, x-ray diffraction analysis shows the appearance of a new phase which is tetragonal (rutile type). Finally, molten germanium dioxide has a vitreous structure, i.e., it is amorphous. Thus, germanium dioxide has three modifications.

The hexagonal (water-soluble) modification converts into the tetragonal (insoluble) modification on
very slow heating, as is apparent from the data of
Table 17. [89]

Table 17, Conversion of the Hexagonal Modification
of Germanium Dioxide Into the Tetragonal Modification.

Temperature, °C	Duration of Heating, hr	Degree of Conversion, %
350	95	97,5
355	117	98,6
360	115	95,2

Crystals of the hexagonal modification of germanium dioxide can be obtained in large sizes, but
the tetragonal modification is always finely divided.
When molten germanium dioxide is cooled slowly,
devitrification accompanied by the formation of the
hexagonal crystalline modification takes place. The
tetragonal form of the dioxide, in contrast to the
two others, is practically insoluble in water and inert

toward acids. Whereas the soluble form has co-ordination numbers 4 and 2, the insoluble form has numbers 6 and 3 and is much denser. [3] The polymorphism is due to the fact that the ratio of the radii of germanium and oxygen, equal to 0.40, is at the limit of these two types of coordination ratios.

It has been suggested that germanium oxide in water forms both solutions of molecular dispersity and colloidal solutions. [3] The pentagermanate ion $(Ge_5O_{11})^{2-}$, which is stable at pH 5.8-8.4, is thought to play an important part in the dissolution of germanium dioxide in aqueous solutions. It is postulated that the residual water present in the solid dioxide in the amount of 3.3% is not water of sorption but water of crystallization, and that the hydrate is pentagermanic acid.

Other authors note that the residual water is adsorbed by solid dioxide, [91] and is not due to the formation of pentagermanate. These statements are

supported by the results of thermographic and x-ray
structural analysis.

In order to obtain water-insoluble germanium
dioxide, a solution of potassium or sodium hydroxide
is added to its solution until the pH is 7. [90]

Table 18 lists the comparative characteristics of
all three modifications of germanium dioxide. [1, 4, 89]

Studies have shown that two crystalline modifications
of germanium dioxide are enantiotropic, i.e., can
each change into the other at a transition point of
$1033 \pm 10^{\circ}$C. [89] The soluble modification has a
stable melting point ($1116 \pm 4^{\circ}$C), and the insoluble
one has a metastable melting point ($1086 \pm 5^{\circ}$C).

Treatment of a solution of tetraethoxygermane in
alcohol with the calculated amount of water yields a
dense precipitate of germanium dioxide hydrate which
can be readily separated from the alcohol. [4] However, methods involving the use of aqueous solutions
are not suitable for the preparation of gels free of

Table 18, Properties of Germanium Dioxide.

Properties	Form		
	Crystalline, Insoluble	Crystalline, Soluble	Vitreous (Amorphous)
Crystal System . . . . Lattice Type	Tetragonal Rutile	Hexagonal α - quartz	Amorphous —
Density at 25°C, g/cm³	6,239	4,228	3,1219
Refractive Index ω . . . . ε	 1,99 2,075	 1,695 1,735	 — 1,607
Melting Point, °C . .	1086 ±5	1116 ±4	—
Solubility, g/100 g of Water at 25°C	0,0023	0,453	0,5184
Reaction With Hydrochloric Acid	Does not react	Forms GeCl₄	Forms GeCl₄
Reaction with 5 N solution of sodium hydroxide at 100°C	Dissolves very slowly	Dissolves rapidly	Dissolves rapidly

other impurities. Hydrolysis of tetrahalides in
water or aqueous solutions of the corresponding
hydrohalic acids always leads to the formation of
crystalline germanium dioxide. The latter is
obtained by treating aqueous solutions of sodium
germanate with hydrochloric acid. A jellylike
precipitate of germanium dioxide is formed when
carbon dioxide is passed through a dilute solution
of sodium germanate. However, the gel is not free
of sodium ions. Like silica gel, germanium dioxide
gel absorbs benzene vapor, ethyl ether and carbon
tetrachloride. [4] The gel can absorb water vapor,
but after the removal of the adsorbed water, its
adsorbing capacity toward benzene decreases. The
colloidal particles constituting the germanium
dioxide gel carry a negative charge. [4]

Germanium dioxide obtained by hydrolyzing a
tetrahalide contains the halogen even after thorough
rinsing. [92] The halogen can be removed by calcining. Uncalcined germanium dioxide free of the
halogen can be obtained only by hydrolyzing ethyl

germanate or by evaporating a pure water extract of the roasted dioxide to dryness.

Data on the solubility in water of germanium dioxide roasted at $600°C$ are given below: [1, 21]

Temp. °C	11	20	26	35	41	100
Solubility, g/100 g of water	0.396	0.430	0.470	0.551	0.617	1.000

In order to determine the pH at the start of precipitation and the solubility product of germanium dioxide, use was made of the polarographic method. [93] The oxidation-reduction potential of the Ge^{2+}/Ge^{4+} system is equal to +0.5 V. Figure 33 shows the variation in the concentration of germanium ions (Ge^{4+}) as a function of the pH of the medium at $22°C$. At pH 5.3-4.1, the concentration of the germanium ions is the highest; as the pH is lowered, it decreases sharply and reaches zero at pH 3.31-3.36. It is apparent that at high pH values germanium is present in the solution in the form of germanate

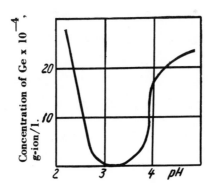

**Fig. 33, Concentration
of Ge^{4+} Versus pH of
Medium.**

ion GeO_3^{2-}. A marked dissolution of germanium
begins again at pH 2.72. The solubility product of
$Ge(OH)_4$ at 22°C, calculated from experimental data,
is 2.39 x 10^{-45}. The solubility of germanic hydroxide   is 6.8 x 10^{-11} mole/1 or 9.56 x 10^{-9} g/1. [93]
When germanium dioxide dissolves, a compound
with four hydroxyl groups is formed. The solubility
of germanium dioxide in perchloric, nitric, hydrochloric, hydrobromic and hydriodic acid at concentrations above 1 M was studied. [203]   Table 19
lists the experimental data obtained.

Table 19, Solubility of Germanium
Dioxide in Inorganic Acids at 25°C.

Acid	Concentration, mole/l	Solubility, mg GeO_2/100 ml	Concentration, mole/l	Solubility, mg GeO_2/100 ml
$HClO_4$	1,56 3,41 5,49	210,0 64,0 12,4	6,92 10,02 11,88	5,2 0,4 0,4
HNO_3	2,15 4,04 4,97 6,07 8,38 10,57	221,8 116,4 81,0 54,0 20,54 7,5	14,40 16,01 18,52 20,14 22,29 24,00	1,9 0,8 0,8 0,6 1,5 1,8
H_2SO_4	1,08 1,77 2,64 3,51 4,11 5,32 6,52	323,2 224,8 136,6 79,5 53,6 26,8 12,8	8,67 11,34 12,63 14,0 15,48 16,63 17,43	6,4 8,4 16,8 23,2 5,8 3,6 2,0
HCl	1,04 2,04 3,17 4,03 5,03 6,03	321,2 228,4 168,8 121,2 113,8 164,4	6,54 6,92 8,15 8,82 9,60 13,39	231,6 311,6 1075,0 419,0 41,0 2,4
HBr	0,72 3,37 5,47 6,90 7,17	315,2 118,6 51,4 85,0 123,0	7,32 7,36 7,60 8,31 8,83	152,2 133,4 69,2 5,4 5,4
HJ	1,27 2,33 3,21 4,17 4,80	286,0 170,8 96,8 60,4 53,6	4,95 4,98 5,20 5,79 7,17	50,0 42,8 11,6 9,2 2,0

In the case of perchloric and nitric acid, the solubility decreases monotonically with rising acid concentration. In sulfuric acid, the solubility also decreases, but at 15 M there is a small maximum. When germanium dioxide dissolves in hydrochloric, hydrobromic and hydriodic acid, maxima are observed. In the case of the first two acids, the maxima follow minima. The abrupt change in solubility may be explained by a change in the composition of the residue. Thus, in solutions of hydrochloric acid the formation of the readily soluble chlorine complexes $GeCl_6^{2-}$ $GeCl_5^-$ takes place when the concentration increases above 5 M. A rise in the acid concentration above 8 M leads to the decomposition of these complexes into insoluble germanium tetrachloride, and to a decrease in the solubility of germanium dioxide (see Table 19).

The results of a study of the solubility of germanium dioxide in hydrofluoric acid are shown in Table 20.[94]

Table 20, Data on The Solubility in the System GeO_2 – HF – H_2O at 25°C.

Analysis of Liquid Phase, wt. %		HF:GeO_2 in Liquid Phase	Analysis of Bottom Phase, wt. %	
HF	GeO_2		HF	GeO_2
1,00	1,55	3,37	—	—
2,00	2,43	4,31	—	—
3,00	3,64	4,32	—	—
7,32	9,14	4,19	—	—
12,48	15,25	4,30	3,45	77,45
13,04	15,93	4,28	—	—
16,03	19,62	4,27	4,23	76,58
22,92	28,90	4,17	—	—
25,40	31,20	4,26	6,35	80,49
26,64	32,50	4,20	—	—
30,00	34,70	4,50	—	—
32,80	39,60	4,30	—	—

As the HF concentration rises to 35%, the solubility of GeO_2 increases linearly, the molar ratio $HF:GeO_2$ in the solution being close to 4, and the solid phase remains constant in composition and consists of germanium dioxide. At an HF concentration of 35%, the composition of the solid phase changes, and in the range of 35 to 41% HF, it corresponds to the formula $GeF_4 \cdot 3H_2O$. This compound separates in the form of very hygroscopic colorless crystals which deliquesce rapidly in air. Its solubility in this range of hydrofluoric acid concentrations is nearly constant. At an HF concentration of 41%, $GeF_4 \cdot 3H_2O$ changes into $H_2GeF_6 \cdot 2H_2O$. The solubility of this very hygroscopic compound decreases with rising HF concentration. The formation of both complex acids is confirmed by electrical conductivity diagrams.

The solubility of oxalic acid $H_2C_2O_4$ in water at $25^\circ C$ is 0.6 mole/l, and that of germanium dioxide, 0.045 mole/l. However, when these two compounds are present together, the solubility of both GeO_2 and $H_2C_2O_4$ increases many times.[95] This is due to the formation of a soluble complex compound. At oxalic acid concentrations up to 5.5 moles/kg, the solid phase in equilibrium is germanium dioxide. At higher concentrations, the formation of germano-oxalic acid takes place. A graph of the solubility in the GeO_2 - $H_2C_2O_4$ - H_2O system is given in Figure 34.[95]

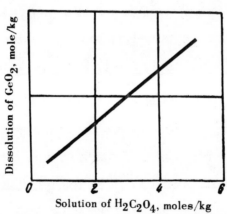

Fig. 34, Solubility in The System $GeO_2 - H_2C_2O_4 - H_2O$ at 25°C.

Tartaric acid dissolves germanium dioxide to form complex tartrates of tetravalent germanium. [1]

Germanium dioxide reacts when fused with ten times its quantity of sodium hydroxide or five times its quantity of sodium carbonate at temperatures above $900°C$. [1] The melts are completely leached out with water. Germanium dioxide dissolves in melts of $Na_2B_4O_7$ and $Na_4P_2O_7$. [1]

The heat of solution of germanium dioxide in water at 12, 22, 32 and $42°C$ is respectively equal to 1310, 2380, 3380 and 3400 cal/mole. [4] In later studies, the heat of solution was found to be 9000 cal/mole. [80]

A study was made of the adsorption of germanium under static and dynamic conditions from aqueous solutions of germanium dioxide on activated birch wood charcoal BAU-1. [96] At low germanium concentrations in the range of 0.0055-0.055 mmole/l, the adsorption is fairly high and amounts respectively to 0.00012 to 0.0012 mole/g, or 89%. The

adsorption equilibrium is established in 2.0-2.5
hours, the bulk being adsorbed in the course of the
first 30 min. The optimum conditions of adsorption
correspond to a pH of 7. A rise in temperature
above the room value impairs this process.

The heat of formation of germanium dioxide at
25°C, determined by burning up germanium,
amounted to -128.1$\pm$0.6 kcal/mole. [4,7,97]

Calorimetric investigations[80] yielded a value for
the heat of formation of solid germanium dioxide
ΔH_{298} = -129.2$\pm$2.0 kcal/mole.

The values cited apparently should be attributed to
the amorphous modification of germanium dioxide.
The crystalline modification with the hexagonal
lattice has a heat of formation ΔH_{298} = -132.3$\pm$1
kcal/mole. [79] The heat capacity of germanium
dioxide may be obtained from the equation [1,97]

$$c_p = 11.2 + 7.7 \times 10^{-3} \ T.$$

The temperature dependence of the heat capacity
of the crystalline and vitreous forms of germanium
dioxide was determined experimentally.[98] The
heat capacity of crystalline germanium dioxide increases from 12.45 cal/mole deg at $298^{O}K$ to 18.2
cal/mole deg at $1325^{O}K$, and, in the case of the
vitreous form, respectively from 12.555 cal/mole
deg at $298^{O}K$ to 19.50 cal/mole deg at $1800^{O}K$. The
temperature dependences are expressed by the following equations:

for crystalline GeO_2 in the range of $298-1350^{O}K$
within $\pm 0.6\%$

$$c_p = 15.00 + 2.86 \times 10^{-3} \, T - 3.02 \times 10^5 \, T^{-2};$$

for amorphous GeO_2 in the range of $298-1800^{O}K$
within $\pm 0.8\%$

$$c_p = 15.68 + 2.38 \times 10^{-3} \, T - 3.40 \times 10^5 \, T^{-2}.$$

The values obtained in[98] for the entropy of germanium dioxide under standard conditions were:

for crystalline GeO_2

$$\Delta S_{298} = 13.2 \pm 0.1 \text{ cal/mole deg;}$$

for amorphous GeO_2

$$\Delta S_{298} = 14.4 \pm 0.1 \text{ cal/mole deg.}$$

The problem of volatilization of germanium dioxide at high temperatures has been studied fairly thoroughly.

The equilibrium vapor pressure over solid germanium dioxide was determined in the range of 934-1087°C by Knudsen's effusion method. [82, 87] Mass-spectrometric studies of the vapor composition over germanium dioxide at 1000°C showed that the main constituents were isomers of germanium monoxide, namely: GeO, $(GeO)_2$ and $(GeO)_3$. [99] The partial pressure of germanium dioxide molecules amounts to only 0.1-0.5% of the total vapor pressure. The amount of free germanium present in the vapors is also negligible. In addition, calculations of the pressure of dissociation of germanium dioxide into germanium and oxygen, carried out below, also confirm the low probability of finding free germanium in the vapor phase:[87]

Temp, $^{\circ}$C	827	927	1027	1077
P_{O_2}, mm Hg.	1.3×10^{-11}	1.5×10^{-9}	1.0×10^{-7}	6.5×10^{-6}

However, the following dissociation occurs[88]

$$GeO_2(g) \longrightarrow GeO(g) + 1/2 O_2(g).$$

According to calculated data,[88] at 1000–1100°C, the equilibrium of this reaction is 90% displaced to the right.

An analysis of the processes which can occur when germanium dioxide is heated above 1000°C,

$$GeO_2(s) \longrightarrow GeO_2(g); \qquad (a)$$
$$GeO_2(s) \longrightarrow GeO(g) + 1/2 O_2(g); \quad (b)$$
$$GeO_2(s) \longrightarrow Ge(s) + O_2(g), \qquad (c)$$

leads to the conclusion that reaction (b) is the most probable; and, since both reaction products are gaseous (the high volatility of germanium monoxide

was discussed above), the composition of the solid
phase after the discharge of the vapors remains
constant, and Knudsen's effusion method is fully
applicable to the investigations.

Germanium dioxide may contain up to 3% of adsorbed
water. [91] It has been stated [100] that in order to
eliminate this water it suffices to calcine the
dioxide at 900°C for several hours. However, later
studies showed that this calcination is not sufficient. [87] Calcination at 800-1000°C at a residual
pressure of about 10^{-6} mm Hg must be carried out
for 50-60 hr in order to completely remove the
traces of moisture. Higher temperatures (1050°C
and higher) make it possible to reduce the necessary
time of calcination to 5-6 hr.

The temperature dependence of the equilibrium
vapor pressure over germanium dioxide is shown
graphically in Figure 35. [82] The experiments involved the use of effusion chambers with aperture
diameters of 0.39 and 0.47 mm. The values obtained

may be called "apparent vapor pressures of germanium dioxide," since they actually represent the pressure of dissociation of the dioxide into germanium monoxide and germanium. On the basis of the experimental data, the dependence of the vapor pressure over germanium dioxide on temperature was calculated:

$$\log P \text{ (mm Hg)} = -\frac{20008}{T} + 12.9693,$$

whence the change in free energy with temperature is

$$\Delta F_T = 91537-46.1749 \ T.$$

The change in heat content and entropy on sublimation will then be

$$\Delta H_T = 91.537 \text{ kcal/mole}$$

and

$$\Delta S_T = 46.175 \text{ cal/mole deg.}$$

In another study,[101] where the effusion method was also used to determine the vapor pressure over germanium dioxide in the range of 1040-1100°C, the following relations were obtained:

$$\log P \text{ (mm Hg)} = - \frac{25517}{T} + 16.245$$

and

$$\Delta H_T = 116.74 \text{ kcal/mole,}$$
$$\Delta S_T = 61.47 \text{ cal/mole deg.}$$

The values of the changes in enthalpy and entropy can be evaluated for the reaction

$$GeO_2 \text{ (s)} \longrightarrow GeO\text{(g)} + 1/2\,O_2.$$

Assuming the values $\Delta H_{298} = -12$ kcal/mole and $\Delta S_{298} = -54.5$ cal/mole deg for gaseous germanium monoxide and $\Delta H_{298} = -128.5$ kcal/mole and $\Delta S_{298} = 13.2$ cal/mole deg for germanium dioxide and taking into account the change in the heat capacities of the substances with temperature, we obtain for the reaction under consideration $\Delta H_{1300^\circ K} = 105.2$ kcal/mole and $\Delta S_{1300^\circ K} = 60.8$ cal/mole deg.

Thus, the calculated values are close to the experimental data obtained in.[101] From the data cited, it follows that the volatility of germanium dioxide is low; thus, at 1000°C the equilibrium vapor pressure does not exceed 10^{-3} mm Hg.

Of interest are data on the reduction of germanium dioxide by hydrogen.[102] The experiments were conducted at $500-650^\circ$C using the circulation method. For the reaction studied

$$GeO_2(s) + 2H_2(g) \longrightarrow Ge(s) + 2H_2O(g),$$

the temperature dependence of the free energy was obtained:

$$\Delta F_T = 13750 - 15.60\ T.$$

An intensive reduction of germanium dioxide by hydrogen to metallic germanium begins at temperatures above 600°C. This is also apparent from the values of the free energies, which become negative above 600°C.

The heat of formation of germanium dioxide calculated from the data obtained $\Delta H_{298} = -132.3 \pm 1.0$ kcal/mole.

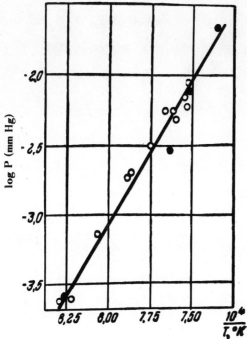

Fig. 35, Temperature Dependence
of Equilibrium Vapor Pressure Over
Germanium Dioxide.

The initial germanium dioxide used in these experiments involving reduction by hydrogen had a hexagonal structure.

In the case of reduction of germanium dioxide by
hydrogen at temperatures above $700^{\circ}C$, an appreciable amount of germanium is lost as the
monoxide. [84,85,103]

The process of reduction of germanium dioxide by
carbon monoxide has a different course. Figure 36
shows the calculated temperature dependences of the
free energies of a series of reactions in the system
germanium dioxide - carbon monoxide. [87] The
calculations were made without taking into account
the changes in the heat capacities of the substances
with temperature, but changes due to the diffusion of
metallic germanium and its oxide were considered.
As can be seen from Figure 36, in the reduction of
germanium dioxide by carbon monoxide, the process
most probable thermodynamically is the reduction to
the lower oxide, and at lower temperatures solid
germanium monoxide should be formed. As the
temperature rises, the volatility of the monoxide
increases abruptly, and thus in the range above $900^{\circ}C$

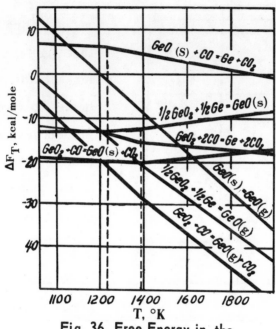

Fig. 36, Free Energy in the
System GeO$_2$ – CO as a
Function of Temperature.

the most probable process is one leading to the
formation of gaseous germanium monoxide. Even
in the case of partial reduction to elemental germanium, the latter can react with excess germanium
dioxide, also causing the formation of germanium
monoxide.

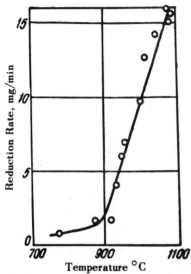

Fig. 37, Temperature Dependence of the Rate of Reduction of Germanium Dioxide by Carbon Monoxide.

Accordingly, ref. [104] indicates that when germanium dioxide is heated to $1000^{\circ}C$ in an atmosphere of carbon monoxide, gaseous germanium monoxide is obtained.

The reduction of germanium dioxide by carbon monoxide was studied with a vacuum unit in which gas circulated in a closed volume at $400-1040^{\circ}C$ and a pressure of 400 mm Hg. [82] The process was controlled by lowering the pressure in the system by freezing out the forming carbon dioxide with liquid nitrogen. At the same time, the quantity of carbon dioxide collected

in the trap and the change in the weight of the original
sample were determined. At temperatures around
1000°C, the weight loss of the sample (see Figure
29) due to the formation and volatilization of germanium monoxide was appreciable. At 1040°C, the
weight loss was 32.5% after 10 min.

The kinetics of reduction of germanium dioxide by
carbon monoxide were also studied by means of the
gas stream method.[105] The initial germanium
dioxide was sufficiently pure and, based on the data
of spectroscopic analysis, contained no more than
10^{-2}% each of calcium, silicon and iron, 10^{-3}%
magnesium, and 10^{-5}% copper. The results of the
studies are shown in Table 21 and are illustrated
in Figure 37. The rate of reduction rises abruptly
at temperatures above 900°C.

The degree of reduction of germanium dioxide by
carbon monoxide varies linearly with time. This
indicates the absence of an inhibiting factor in the
reduction, such as a surface layer of a solid re-

Table 21, Temperature Dependence of the Rate of Oxidation of Germanium Dioxide by Carbon Dioxide.

Temperature °C	Reduction Rate mg/min	Degree of Reduction After 20 min, %	Temperature °C	Reduction Rate mg/min	Degree of Reduction After 20 min, %
770	0,86	3,21	1000	9,74	39,00
870	1,62	6,50	1010	12,72	51,00
914	1,77	7,04	1049	14,25	57,00
928	4,05	18,23	1076	15,90	63,70
944	6,03	24,10	1079	15,00	60,00
953	6,92	27,70	1083	15,55	62,00

action product. At the temperatures of the investigations such a product could have been elemental germanium. Under these conditions, germanium monoxide is very volatile and therefore does not accumulate on the sample. X-ray structural analysis of the residue of the reduction showed only the lines of germanium dioxide with a quartz-type lattice.

The high weight loss of the samples upon reduction of germanium dioxide by carbon monoxide may be explained only by the volatilization of germanium monoxide. To confirm this hypothesis, the sublimates were collected and oxidized with hydrogen peroxide in a medium of ammonia with heating. The weight increase varied from 15.3 to 22.0%. The calculated value is 18.05%. Some deviations in weight gain were attributed to the small samples of the collected sublimate (10-20 mg) and hence, to an insufficiently accurate analysis.

The kinetics of reduction of germanium dioxide by carbon were studied in the range of 970-1070°C in a vacuum device with a quartz spring balance. [105]

The results of the experiments were used to plot the curves shown in Figures 38 and 39. The rate of reduction of germanium dioxide by carbon increased markedly at temperatures above 1000°C. This increase in the rate of the process cannot be attributed to the volatilization of graphite or germanium dioxide (see Figure 38). X-ray structural analysis of the residues of the reduction showed only the lines of germanium dioxide with a quartz-type lattice.

All of the above indicates that in the case of reduction of germanium dioxide by carbon monoxide, the abrupt increase in the rate of the reaction between germanium dioxide and graphite is due to the formation and volatilization of germanium monoxide. Calculations confirm the probability of such a process at temperatures above 800°C. [79]

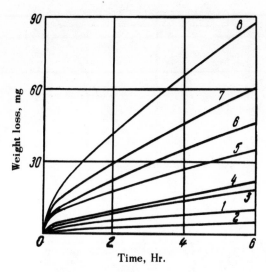

Fig. 38, Isotherms of Variation in
Weight Loss of Sample During Re-
duction of Germanium Dioxide by
Carbon in a Vacuum.

1—GeO_2 at $1070°C$; 2—Carbon at $1070°C$;
3—Sample at $970°C$; 4—Same, $990°C$; 5—
same, $1010°C$; 6—same, $1030°C$; 7—same
$1050°C$; 8—same, $1070°C$;

The reaction of germanium dioxide with aluminum
was studied qualitatively.[103] A germanium yield
of about 60% was thus obtained.

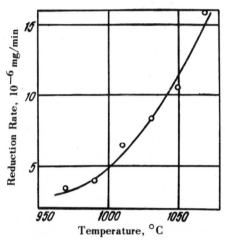

Fig. 39. Temperature Dependence
of the Rate of Reduction of Germanium Dioxide by Carbon in a
Vacuum.

The rate of reaction of germanium dioxide with iron
was studied in a vacuum device with a spring
balance.[106] The rate of the process was estimated
from the weight loss with time at a constant temperature and a pressure of 10^{-2} mm Hg. The starting
materials were germanium dioxide of grade TsMTU
3431-55 and reduced metallic iron of grade TU-MZ-
10-58. Both preparations were comminuted to 0.074
mm.

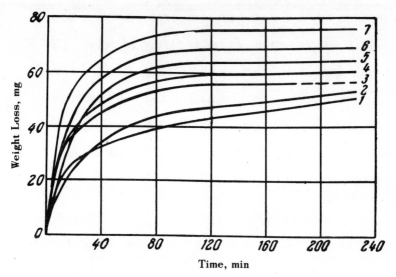

Fig. 40, Temperature Dependence of the Rate of Reaction
of Germanium Dioxide with Iron.

1 – at 930°C, 2 – 950°C; 3 – 990°C; 4 – 1010°C; 5 – 1030°C;
6 – 1050°C; 7 – 1070°C

The measurements were made in the range of
930-1070°C. As is evident from Figure 40, the
rate of reaction of germanium dioxide with iron
changes appreciably with temperature and at 950-
1000°C the reaction proceeds fairly rapidly. The
weight loss in the temperature range studied may be
explained only by the formation and volatilization of
germanium monoxide. Germanium, iron, germanium dioxide, and also iron oxides have low
vapor pressures at 930-1070°C. [12, 107]

X-ray structural analyses have shown the complete absence of elemental germanium in the sample,
and the phases GeO_2, Fe, Fe_3O_4 and Fe_2O_3 were
identified.

It is known that germanium forms solid solutions
with iron over a wide concentration range (up to
20 at.%), [50] and at 30 and 65 at.% yields chemical
compounds, respectively, Fe_2Ge and $FeGe_2$. Data
on the change in the lattice parameters of iron
caused by the dissolution of germanium therein

make it possible to estimate qualitatively the mig-
ration of germanium into iron during their interaction at high temperatures. Standard samples of
solid solutions with concentrations of germanium
in iron of 5, 10 and 15% were prepared.

Phase analysis showed the presence of the σ phase
of iron in the samples, and the x-ray diffraction
pattern of the sample with 15% germanium showed
one line of an unidentified phase. The calculation
error did not exceed $\pm 2\%$ germanium in the solid
solution. The changes of the lattice parameter are
shown in Figure 41. When germanium dissolves in
iron, the lattice parameter of the latter increases
steadily.

On the basis of the dependence obtained, a determination was made of the solubility of germanium
in iron in samples obtained from reduction experiments. The solubility of germanium was found to
be 4-10%. This shows that despite the formation
and volatilization of germanium monoxide, when

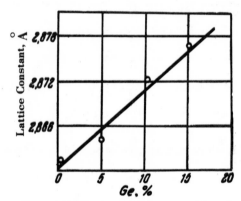

Fig. 41, Lattice Parameters Versus
Composition of Solid Solution of
Germanium in Iron.

germanium dioxide interacts with iron at high temperatures (up to 1070°C), a partial reduction to
elemental germanium occurs. The latter is readily
dissolved by excess metallic iron.

An x-ray structural analysis was performed on
samples obtained from experiments in which the
weight ratio GeO_2:Fe was varied; the results are
given below:

Ratio GeO_2:Fe	1:3	1:1
Phases detected	Fe, FeO	GeO_2, FeO, Fe_3O_4

Ratio GeO_2:Fe	3:1	7:1
Phases detected	GeO_2, Fe_2O_3	GeO_2, Fe_2O_3

It is apparent from these data that when iron is present in excess, ferrous oxide (FeO) is obtained; in the presence of smaller amounts of the reductant, ferrosoferric oxide (Fe_3O_4) and even ferric oxide (Fe_2O_3) is formed. Thermodynamic calculations confirm the likelihood of the occurrence of these processes.

It is known that germanium dioxide reacts to an appreciable extent with carbon tetrachloride at $500°C$:[4]

$$GeO_2 + CCl_4 \longrightarrow GeCl_4 + CO_2;$$
$$GeO_2 + 2CCl_4 \longrightarrow GeCl_4 + 2COCl_2.$$

The reaction between germanium dioxide and lithium hydride leads to a reduction with the formation of germanium monoxide and elemental germanium.[4]

The above material shows that germanium dioxide is in many ways similar to silicon dioxide.

5. GERMANATES

Although the coordination number of silicon in quartz is 4, that of germanium in crystals of germanium dioxide is both 4 and 6 (tetragonal and hexagonal structure). The same pattern prevails in the composition of germanates. In addition to a tetrahedral structure (GeO_4), analogous to silicates, there is an octahedral structure (GeO_6), analogous to stannates.

By analogy with silicates, the following classification of germanates may be made:[108]

(a) Mesogermanates: $Be(GeO_4)$, $Zn_2(GeO_4)$, $Ca_2(GeO_4)$, $CaMg(GeO_4)$, $Ce(GeO_4)$, $Zr(GeO_4)$, $U(GeO_4)$;

(b) Zorogermanates of the type of $Sc_2(Ge_2O_7)$;

(c) Cyclogermanates: $BaTi(Ge_3O_9)_2$, $K_2(GeO_3)$, $Rb_2(GeO_3)$, $Cs_2(GeO_3)$, $Cu(GeO_3)$;

(d) Inogermanates: $CaMg(GeO_3)_2$, $K_2(GeO_3)$, $Rb_2(GeO_3)$, $Cs_2(GeO_3)$, $Cu(GeO_3)$;

(e) Philogermanates: $Mg_3((OH)_2 Ge_2O_4)$, $Ni_3((OH)_2 Ge_4O_{10})$, $Ni_6((OH)_8 Ge_4O_{10})$;

(f) Tectogermanates: $KNa_3(AlGeO_4)$, $K(AlGe_2O_6)$, $Na(AlGe_3O_8)$, $Na(GaGe_3O_8)$, $Ca(Al_2GeSiO_8)$, $Ba(Al_2Ge_2O_8)$.

If an aqueous solution of germanium dioxide is added to a 2 N solution of potassium chloride or nitrate, potassium pentagermanate $K_2Ge_5O_{11}$ precipitates at pH 9.2. [3] Thallium pentagermanate can be obtained in similar fashion. All the germanates studied (of lithium, sodium, potassium, ammonium, lutetium, cesium, silver, and thallium) were found to be isostructural. The methods of their preparation are given in Table 22.

Table 22, Methods of Preparation of Zeolitic Germanates

Ion	by Hydrolysis (Me_2GeO_3)	by Hydrothermal Synthesis at 200°	by Hydrolysis ($Me_2Ge_4O_9$)	From other Compounds
Li⁺	+	+	+	—
Na⁺	+	+	+	$Na_2H_2 \cdot GeO_4 \cdot 6H_2O$
K⁺	+	+	+	—
NH₄⁺	—	+	—	Exchange of NH_4^+ ions
Rb⁺	+	+	+	$GeO_2 + 25\%\ NH_3$
Cs⁺	+	+	+	—
Ag⁺	—	—	—	
Tl⁺	+	+	—	Exchange of NH_4^+ ions

Although the radii of the Me$^+$ ions differ appreciably the lattice parameters remain nearly constant. The structure of these compounds is characterized by a combination of octahedra (GeO$_6$) and tetrahedra (GeO$_4$). This explains the zeolitic properties of these compounds, which are characterized by a weak bonding with the water of crystallization. The interatomic distances Ge-O in zeolitic germanates are 1.67 Å (for the tetrahedral structure) and 1.19 Å (for the octahedral structure).

The heat of dehydration of sodium germanate is equal to 11.1 kcal/mole, and that of potassium germanate, to 10.9 kcal/mole, which indicates weak bonding with the water of crystallization.

Thermal, x-ray structural, and microscopic analyses were used to study the GeO$_2$ - Li$_2$O system.[109] The existence of two compounds was observed: Li$_2$GeO$_3$ with a melting point of 1237° and Li$_4$GeO$_4$ with a melting point of 1298°C (Figure 42). The melting point of pure germanium

dioxide was $1115 \pm 3^{\circ}$C. Thermographic investigations
showed that at 920-930°C in compositions containing
55-70 mole % germanium dioxide, there is observed
an endothermic effect which corresponds to the
melting point of the eutectic mixture $Li_2GeO_3 + GeO_2$.
A eutectic point with the composition 60% Li_2O
and 40% GeO_2 and having a melting point of
$1115 \pm 3^{\circ}$C was found between the compounds
Li_2GeO_3 and Li_4GeO_4. The region with an Li_2O
content of about 70% was not studied because corrosion of the platinum crucible and thermocouple
occurred.

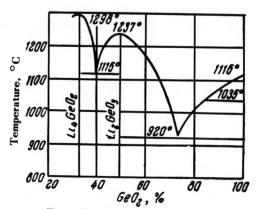

Fig. 42, Phase Diagram of the
System $GeO_2 - Li_2O$.

The initial germanium dioxide had a tetragonal body-centered lattice with parameters a = 4.388 Å and c = 2.859 Å.

X-ray structural analysis showed that Li_2GeO_3 has a body-centered cubic lattice with parameter a = 6.795 Å.

The phase diagram of the GeO_2 - Na_2O system has been studied[110] (Figure 43). The formation of two compounds, Na_2GeO_3 and $Na_2Ge_4O_9$, which melted without decomposition at $1060° \pm 5°C$ and $1080° \pm 5°C$ respectively, was established. Two eutectics were found: one with a melting point of $905 \pm 5°C$ (92.5% GeO_2), and one with a melting point of $785 \pm 5°C$ (66.6% GeO_2).

The existence of sodium pentagermanate $Na_2Ge_2O_5$ in this system[4] was disputed in several studies.[110, 111] The interaction between germanium dioxide and sodium oxide was studied in the range of $100-400°C$ by use of autoclaves at pressures of 12 tech. atm.[111] The existence of the compounds

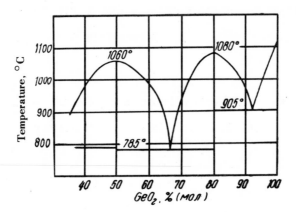

Fig. 43, Phase Diagram of the
System GeO_2 – Na_2O.

$Na_3HGe_7O_{16} \cdot 4H_2O$ and $Na_2Ge_4O_9$, which have
different optical and physicochemical properties,
was established.

The most probable composition of the germanate
is $Na_3HGe_7O_{16} \cdot 4H_2O$ instead of the $Na_2Ge_5O_{11}$

or $NaH_3Ge_2O_6$ proposed earlier.

Experiments have shown that the process of decomposition of the germanate proceeds according
to the equation

$$2Na_3HGe_7O_{16} \cdot 4H_2O \longrightarrow 3Na_2Ge_4O_9 + 9H_2O +$$

$$2GeO_2;$$

free germanium dioxide was determined by x-ray
analysis.

Sodium metagermanate Na_2GeO_3 can be obtained
by fusing germanium dioxide with sodium carbonate
in the proportion of 1:1 at the melting point of the
latter. [4] A white crystalline substance is thus
obtained which absorbs carbon dioxide in air.
Sodium metagermanate dissolves well in water to
form a strongly alkaline solution, and hydrolyzes
to form germanium hydroxide. Evaporation of a
solution of sodium metagermanate produces the
heptahydrate $Na_2GeO_3 \cdot 7H_2O$. When freshly prepared, it dissolves in water completely, forming an
alkaline solution. However, a partial dehydration or
roasting of the heptahydrate causes conversion into

an insoluble form. Its solubility in terms of sodium
metagermanate at 0°C is 14 g per 100 g of water,
and at 25°C, 25.9 g per 100 g of water. The vapor
pressure of water over the crystal hydrate is 4 mm
Hg at 20°C.

In contrast to sodium germanate, potassium metagermanate K_2GeO_3 is not formed when germanium
dioxide is used with potassium carbonate. [4] The
emf of germanate solutions at a ratio of Na:Ge = 2
was determined from measurements of the emf of
sodium hydroxide in solutions of Glauber's salt. [112]
The solutions contain $(H_3GeO_4)^-$ and $(H_2GeO_4)^{2-}$
ions. The second dissociation constant of
$Na_2(H_2GeO_4)$ in water was found to be 4.87 x 10^{-13}.
It was established that germanic acid in melts of
Glauber's salt is twice or even three times as
strong as in water.

Experiments have shown that sodium hydroxide is
completely dissociated in melts of Glauber's salt and
that its activity is then equal to 1. The addition of

pure germanium dioxide to the melt at the above-
indicated ratio made it possible to determine the
degree of dissociation of the germanate: it is very
low and does not exceed 0.36% (Figure 44).

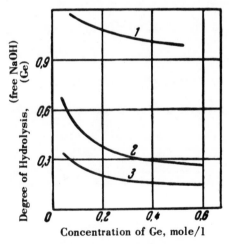

Fig. 44, Degree of Hydrolysis of
$Na_2(H_2GeO_4)$ in Molten Glauber's
Salt (3), Water (2) and of $Na_3(HGeO_4)$
in Molten Glauber's Salt (1).

With most oxides of divalent elements, germanium dioxide forms <u>ortho</u> compounds ($\underline{Me}_2GeO_4$).

The system CuO - GeO_2 was studied by the thermal and x-ray methods. Samples with 15, 25, 33, 50, 66 and 75% CuO were prepared.[113] The reaction of copper oxide with germanium dioxide takes place in the range of 800 to $1000^\circ C$. This system contains only one compound, $CuGeO_3$, which is blue-green in color. Copper metagermanate does not melt in air at atmospheric pressure, and at $1179-1200^\circ C$ dissociates with the evolution of oxygen.

From the phase diagram (Figure 45) it is evident that the reaction of lead oxide with germanium dioxide forms the metagermanate $PbGeO_3$, which melts congruently at $795^\circ C$, and the germanate Pb_3GeO_5, which melts congruently at $738^\circ C$.[114] Between these germanates there is a phase with a smooth fusion maximum at $738^\circ C$. The composition $Pb_5Ge_3O_{11}$ may be attributed to this phase.

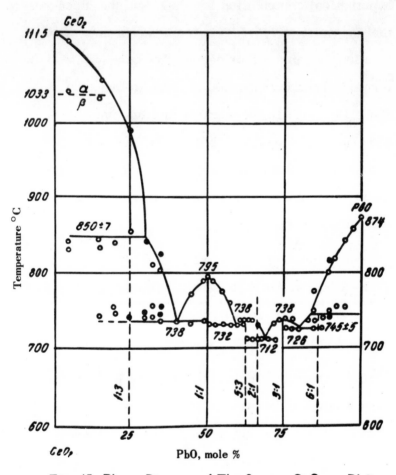

Fig. 45, Phase Diagram of The System GeO$_2$ – PbO

In the region rich in lead oxide, a germanate of the
hypothetical composition Pb_6GeO_8 with an incongruent
melting point of $745\pm5^{o}C$ is formed. In the region
rich in germanium dioxide, a polycompound is
formed whose composition is close to that of
$PbGe_3O_7$, with an incongruent melting point of
$850\pm7^{o}C$. The melts of this region have a high
viscosity. Melts containing from 45 to 100% lead
oxide are mobile and crystallize at comparatively
low temperatures.

A comparison of the diagrams of $PbO - SiO_2$ and
$PbO - GeO_2$ shows that the crystallochemical similarity between silicon and germanium is weakly expressed in lead silicates and germanates.

Calcium germanates can be obtained by sintering
germanium dioxide with calcium oxide or carbonate
at $1000^{o}C$ in an oxygen atmosphere; an orthogermanate is thus formed. [115] Another method of
preparation is the combination of aqueous solutions
of sodium germanate and calcium chloride, or

neutralization of dilute germanic acid with lime milk. After prolonged boiling with a reflux condenser in a carbon dioxide-free atmosphere, an amorphous precipitate is obtained which, after roasting for 2.5 hours at $600^{\circ}C$, converts into a crystalline metagermanate.

A study of the systems[115] Na_2GeO_3 - $Ca(NO_3)_2$ - H_2O and Na_2GeO_3 - $Fe(NO_3)_3$ - H_2O established the formation of calcium metagermanate $CaO \cdot GeO_2 \cdot n-H_2O$ and three iron germanates: Fe_2O_3 - $GeO_2 \cdot H_2O$, $Fe_2O_3 \cdot 2GeO_2 \cdot n-H_2O$, and $Fe_2O_3 \cdot 3GeO_2 \cdot n-H_2O$. Their existence was confirmed by the results of thermographic and x-ray diffraction analyses. Calcium germanate $CaO \cdot GeO_2$, white with a greenish hue, was obtained; its crystal lattice belongs to the triclinic system and its indices of refraction are $N_g = 1.734$ and $N_p = 1.724$.[116] For its preparation, the mixture of calcium oxide and germanium dioxide was wetted with water (10%), pelleted, and kept for 3 hours at $1250^{\circ}C$.

The coprecipitation of germanium dioxide with iron hydroxide was studied. The results are shown in Table 23. [117]

The coprecipitation is more complete when the solution is neutralized with ammonia.

Table 23, Coprecipitation of Germanium with Iron Hydroxide.

Molar Ratio Fe₂O₃ : GeO₂	Precipitation of Germanium on Nautralization, %	
	NaOH	Na H₄OH
1:4	90,4	94,1
2:3	96,9	97,2
3:2	99,7	99,8
4:1	99,8	99,9

The precipitates obtained were dried to constant weight and subjected to thermographic and x-ray diffraction analyses. The thermogram of pure germanium dioxide showed two dehydration effects (in the range of 100-200°C). The thermogram of the

mixtures $Fe_2O_3:GeO_2 = 1:4$ has an endothermic
dehydration effect at $200-230°C$ and two exothermic
effects (620 and $800°C$). The x-ray pattern of the
product calcined at $620°C$ has new lines probably
belonging to the compound $2Fe_2O_3 \cdot 7GeO_2$.

The thermogram of the precipitate $Fe_2O_3:GeO_2 =$
2:3 displays endothermic effects (200 and $400°C$),
exothermic effects (610 and $680°C$), and a decomposition effect ($910°C$). The experiments showed
that on heating to $1400°C$, the water of crystallization and hygroscopic water were eliminated. In the
range of $610-680°C$, a germanate ($2Fe_2O_3 \cdot 3GeO_2$)
crystallizes, and at $900-910°C$ this germanate breaks
down to form $2Fe_2O_3 \cdot 7GeO_2$ and Fe_2O_3. The
thermograms and x-ray patterns of mixtures of
compositions 3:2 and 4:1 differ only slightly from
one other.

Mixtures of dry oxides in the same proportions
were calcined at 700 and $900°C$ for 6-12 hours.[117]
The x-ray patterns of the products contained lines of

only pure iron oxides and germanium oxides, i.e.,
the dry oxides had not reacted.

A study was made of the compounds formed by the
reaction of germanium dioxide with oxides of
aluminum and gallium at temperatures above
1200°C. [118] Compounds of the type of mullite and
andalusite were obtained whose characteristics are
listed in Table 24.

The compound $3Al_2O_3 \cdot 2GeO_2$ is very similar in
structure to mullite $(3Al_2O_3 \cdot 2SiO_2)$, but, owing to
the larger radius of the tetravalent germanium ions,
a certain increase in lattice is observed.

A compound of the composition $Na_2O \cdot Al_2O_3 \cdot$
$2GeO_2$ was obtained. [119] Hexafluogermanates of
the composition $\underline{Me}GeF_6 \cdot 6H_2O$ (where $\underline{Me}$ is Mg,
Zn, Cd, Fe, Co, Ni and Mn) and $\underline{Me}GeF_6 \cdot 2H_2O$
(where $\underline{Me}$ is Sr, Ca) were synthesized. [120] Since
they all dissolve well in water, their solutions were
first obtained by reacting the metals or carbonates
with a solution of fluogermanic acid where

$HF:GeO_2 = 6$. The solutions of fluogermanates obtained were filtered and evaporated. The crystals formed were dried in air. All the fluogermanates except the calcium salt were obtained in the form of large, well-formed crystals. Thermograms recorded during the heating of the fluogermanates showed that dehydration occurs first and is followed by the decomposition of the salts into $\underline{MeF}_2$ and GeF_4. A part of germanium tetrafluoride volatilizes, and is converted into the dioxide by hydrolysis.

Hexafluogermanates of divalent metals are more stable than hexafluosilicates. This is due to the more pronounced metallic properties of germanium.

Sodium and potassium thiogermanates were obtained. [4] This was done by adding freshly precipitated germanium sulfide to a concentrated aqueous solution of the sulfide of the corresponding alkali metal, and by pouring the mixture into acetone. The salts $K_2Ge_2S_7 \cdot 9H_2O$ and $Na_6Ge_2S_7 \cdot 9H_2O$ crystallize upon slow evaporation in a hydrogen

sulfide atmosphere at room temperature. They
decompose rapidly in air.

6. GERMANIUM SULFIDES

The phase diagram of the system germanium -
sulfur has not been described in the literature.
However, abundant data are available on sulfide
compounds of germanium.

Germanium Monosulfide

Germanium monosulfide can be obtained both by the
wet and the dry method. In the wet method, germanium monosulfide is precipitated by hydrogen
sulfide from aqueous solutions containing compounds
of divalent germanium. When hydrogen sulfide is
passed through a hot hydrochloric acid solution of
divalent germanium, a dark-red precipitate
separates. [76] A light-yellow monosulfide precipitates from the cold solution. The amorphous
sulfide obtained may be converted into the crystalline state by heating in an inert atmosphere to 450°C.
The crystalline monosulfide is black.

The density of the dark-red germanium monosulfide
is 3.31 g/cm^3. [76] It dissolves relatively easily in
dilute hydrochloric acid, but reacts weakly with
sulfuric, phosphoric, or organic acids. Germanium
monosulfide is rapidly oxidized by hot, dilute nitric
acid and aqueous solutions of hydrogen peroxide,
potassium permanganate, chlorine and bromine,
and dissolves readily in solutions of alkalis or sulfides, forming red solutions. Chlorine reacts with
the sulfide at room temperature, forming germanium
tetrachloride.

With hydrogen chloride vapors, the monosulfide
begins to react at an appreciable rate at temperatures
above 150°C.

Germanium sulfide can be obtained by the dry
method from germanite, [121] which is preheated at
800°C in a stream of nitrogen in order to remove the
arsenic. Ammonia is then passed over the powder at
825°C. There is formation and volatilization of germanium monosulfide, which can be collected in a condenser.

Another method of preparing germanium monosulfide consists in reducing germanium disulfide
with hydrogen. [77] When metallic germanium is
heated in a stream of hydrogen sulfide at 850°C,
there is also formation and volatilization of germanium monosulfide. [122] The sublimate is a
mixture of steel-gray acicular and lamellar crystals
which are black in the pulverized state.

Finally, germanium monosulfide can be obtained
by the action of a mixture of hydrogen sulfide and
hydrogen on germanium dioxide powder at temperatures above 700°C. [77] Such a monosulfide has
a density of 3.78-4.01 g/cm^3 at 20°C. [4,76] Its
hardness is approximately 2 on the Mohs scale.
Data exist on the melting point of germanium monosulfide: 530°C, [4,123] 615°[124] and even
625°C. [7,76] The value of the melting point which
should be considered most probable is 615°C. It
was determined from the inflection of the curve
representing the change in the vapor pressure of

germanium monosulfide with the temperature and
plotted in the coordinates log vapor pressure vs.
reciprocal temperature. The heat of fusion of germanium monosulfide is equal to 6 kcal/mole;[124] the
change in entropy on melting is 6.75 cal/mole deg.

Crystalline monosulfide is slowly oxidized by an
ammonia solution of hydrogen peroxide, chlorine
water, and a solution of potassium permanganate.[76]
It reacts slowly with acids and alkalis even on
boiling.[4] However, when pulverized into a fine
powder, the monosulfide dissolves appreciably in
solutions of caustic alkalis and reacts with hydrochloric acid. It is sparingly soluble in ammonia,
and this is utilized to remove germanium disulfide
from the monosulfide; the disulfide goes into
solution even in the cold.[74, 125]

The monosulfide has a high volatility at temperatures above 500°C.[76] The vapor pressure of
germanium monosulfide has been studied by several
authors. The results obtained are compared in Table

25. From this table it is apparent that the results
of experiments carried out by different authors are
in mutual agreement.

By averaging the data obtained, one can derive an
equation for the 300-615°C range:

$$\log P \text{ (mm Hg)} = - \frac{8335}{T} + 10.612.$$

The averaged data are very close to the results
obtained in.[129] The values found for the change in
enthalpy and entropy on sublimation of germanium
monosulfide are $\Delta H_T = 38200$ cal/mole and $\Delta S_T =$
36.1 cal/mole deg.

The results of all these studies were treated by
assuming that monomeric molecules of germanium
monosulfide were involved in the sublimation. The
close agreement of the results obtained by the different methods bears out this assumption.

No consideration was given in the calculations to
the possible dissociation of germanium monosulfide
upon heating. As was shown by experiments on the

determination of the dissociation pressure of germanium monosulfide, carried out by the transport
method, this process is not appreciably developed in
the range of 390-485°C. The dissociation pressure
of germanium monosulfide with the formation of germanium and sulfur is given by the equation.[132]

$$\log P_{S_2} \text{ (mm Hg)} = - \frac{13612}{T} + 9.527.$$

The vapor pressure of sulfur given by this equation
does not exceed 1×10^{-3} mm Hg even at 500°C, i.e.,
the dissociation may be neglected in the calculations.

The vapor pressure over molten germanium monosulfide was measured by the transport method
in nitrogen at 617-662°C.[124] The data obtained are
described by the equation

$$\log P \text{ (mm Hg)} = - \frac{6398}{T} + 8.70$$

At 662°C, the vapor pressure of germanium monosulfide is 68.2 mm Hg. The boiling point of germanium monosulfide, found by extrapolating the above
equation,[124] is 826°C.

Table 24, Lattice Constants and Density of Germanium Compounds.

Compound	Lattice Constants, A			Density, g/cm³
	a	b	c	
$3Al_2O_3 \cdot 2GeO_2$	7,64	7,76	2,92	3,62
$2Al_2O_3 \cdot GeO_2$	7,67	7,76	2,92	3,63
$3Ga_2O_3 \cdot 2GeO_2$	7,87	8,00	3,01	5,01
$Ga_2O_3 \cdot GeO_2$	8,11	8,27	5,80	4,98

A study of the sublimation rate of germanium monosulfide by using Langmuir's effusion method was
made in the range of 400-550°C. [131] As is apparent
from Figure 46, the volatilization rate of the monosulfide increases sharply with the temperature. Thus,
at 550°C, the sublimation rate of germanium monosulfide is 735 kg/m^2 day.

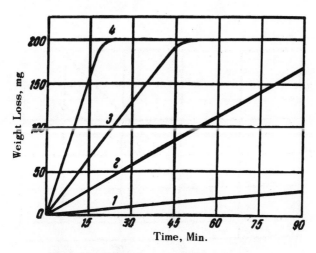

Fig. 46, Temperature Dependence of
The Volatilization Rate of Germanium
Monosulfide:
1—at 400°C; 2—450°C; 3—500°C; 4—550°C.

Germanium monosulfide is oxidized by oxygen. An approximate thermodynamic analysis of the reactions of oxidation of germanium monosulfide to germanous sulfate and germanium dioxide showed that the first process is more probable below 380°C.[87] This is shown clearly in Figure 47. Germanous sulfate is thermodynamically stable below 380°C.

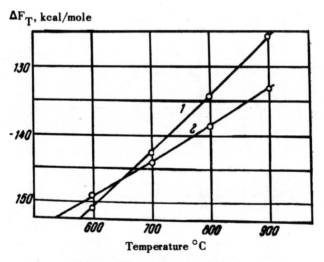

Fig. 47, Free Energy Change on Oxidation of Germanium Monosulfide.

Experiments on the oxidation of germanium monosulfide were carried out in a vacuum unit in which
air was circulated in a closed volume. The initial
pressure in the system was 400 mg Hg. The consumption of oxygen by the oxidation was measured
by the decrease in the pressure of the system. The
amount of sulfur dioxide formed was determined by
freezing it out continuously in a trap cooled with
liquid nitrogen. The measurements were made in
the range of 200-545°C. [82, 87] At higher temperatures, germanium monosulfide volatilized considerably. Figure 48 shows the change in the oxidation rate of germanium monosulfide with temperature: below 350°C, the consumption of atmospheric
oxygen was less than that required for the formation
of sulfur dioxide in the case of oxidation of the initial
sulfide to the oxide. Oxygen probably remains bound
to the surface of the sample being oxidized, i.e., the
sulfate is formed. Above 350°C, the consumption of
atmospheric oxygen is equal to the weight of the
sulfur dioxide formed. This relationship is observed

in the oxidation according to the reaction

$$GeS + 2O_2 \longrightarrow GeO_2 + SO_2,$$

where the molecular weight of SO_2 is equal to the
molecular weight of two oxygen molecules.

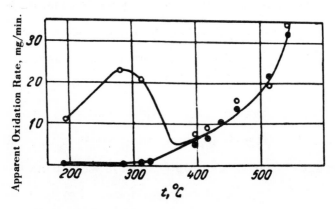

Fig. 48, Variation of the Oxidation Rate of
Germanium Monosulfide with Temperature.
(time, 10 min):

0 — based on the consumption of atmospheric oxygen;
0 — based on the formation of sulfur dioxide.

Indeed, during the oxidation of the black powder of germanium monosulfide above 350°C, the formation of a white powder of germanium dioxide was observed in the surface layer. The oxidation rate rises sharply at about 500°C. The oxidation isotherm (Figure 49) shows that the oxidation rate of the monosulfide is high in the beginning, then decreases rapidly. This is due to the formation of the involatile germanium dioxide on the surface.

The thermogravimetric method[133, 134] was used to obtain data on the oxidation of germanium mono-sulfide by air. An appreciable oxidation of germanium monoxide begins at 350°C. A sharp increase in the oxidation rate was observed at $560-570^{\circ}$C. In the range from 350 to 580°C, the weight of the initial sample (100 mg) increases by 2.3 mg. This fact is attributed to a partial formation of germanium sulfate. However, the main product of the oxidation is germanium dioxide.

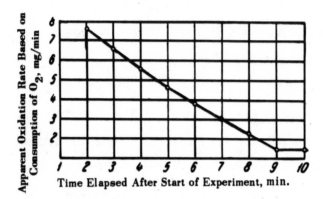

Fig. 49, Oxidation Isotherm of Germanium
Monosulfide at 545°C.

The principal thermodynamic characteristics of
germanium monosulfide are: dissociation energy of
the monosulfide, determined from spectroscopic
data, 130.5±3.0 kcal/mole;[1, 126] heat of formation
of solid germanium monosulfide at 25°C, obtained
by calculation, 25.8±8.5 kcal/mole.[126] The heat
capacity of crystalline germanium monosulfide may
be calculated from the approximate equation:[126]

$$C_p = 8.10 + 10.88 \times 10^{-3}T.$$

The temperature dependence of the heat capacity of the gaseous monosulfide in the range of 25-427°C is described by the equation:[126]

$$C_p = 8.873 - 7.394 \times 10^4 T^{-2}.$$

A determination of the entropy of crystalline germanium monosulfate at 25°C gave 16.3 cal/mole deg. [126]

The standard heat of formation of gaseous germanium monosulfide, calculated by taking into account the heat of formation of the crystalline modification as well as the heat capacities and the heat of sublimation, is equal to 12200 cal/mole.[129]

Germanium Disulfide

Germanium disulfide is insoluble in strongly acidic media. This property led to the discovery of the element germanium. A. Winkler thought that the element being sought should precipitate as the sulfide from a weakly acidic solution. He was unable to carry out the precipitation under these conditions.

Winkler then added a large quantity of acid to the solution; this caused the immediate precipitation of heavy white flakes which were subsequently identified as germanium disulfide. [4] The method of preparing germanium disulfide by precipitation with hydrogen sulfide from a strongly acidic solution is also utilized today, with some modifications: germanium dioxide is dissolved in 6 N hydrochloric acid and hydrogen sulfide is passed through the solution. Even after consecutive washing with 6 N hydrochloric acid, alcohol, and ether, the white flocculent precipitate of germanium disulfide may contain up to 2-3% moisture. [92, 134] After roasting in nitrogen at 300°, a crystalline powder is formed which in chemical composition is close to the stoichiometry of germanium disulfide. [124]

Better results are obtained in the synthesis of germanium disulfide by the dry method. This synthesis can be carried out directly from the elements by passing sulfur vapor over germanium powder at

$1000-1100^{\circ}$C. [124] Another method consists in reacting a mixture of hydrogen sulfide and sulfur
vapor with germanium powder at 850°C. [135,136]
The germanium disulfide formed is collected in a
condenser. The disulfide is also obtained by sub-
liming germanium monosulfide in sulfur vapor. [136]
When germanium dioxide is heated to 850°C in
sulfur vapor, a reaction takes place which forms germanium disulfide. [4] Finally, germanium disulfide
also forms as a result of the reaction between dry
gaseous germanium tetrachloride and hydrogen
sulfide at $600-650^{\circ}$C. [137]

Germanium disulfide obtained in the dry manner
(by any of the above methods) is close to the stoichiometric composition. The color of the crystals
is pearl-white with a silvery or mother-of-pearl
luster on the cleavage planes. [136] The individual
plates of the disulfide are flexible, flaky, and
greasy to the touch. The cleavage is perfect along
(001) and less so along (010). The Mohs hardness

is 2.0-2.5. The density at 20°C is equal to 2.70-
2.94 g/cm^3. [92,136]

Germanium disulfide does not dissolve to any
appreciable extent in cold or hot sulfuric, hydrochloric, or nitric acid. [136] However, it dissolves
well in alkalis, particularly in the presence of
hydrogen peroxide. On heating in air, germanium
disulfide darkens and decomposes with the evolution
of hydrogen sulfide. Under the microscope, the
crystals of germanium disulfide appear as pris-
matic pinacoidal tablets of hexagonal shape belonging to the rhombic system. [136] The lattice
constants are a = 11.66 Å, b = 22.34 Å, and c =
6.86 Å. [125] X-ray structural data also confirm
the rhombic structure of the lattice of germanium
disulfide. The refractive index in yellow light
N_g = 2.30 and N_p = 2.25. The melting point of
germanium disulfide determined in sealed ampules
is 825±3°C. [137] According to other data, the
melting point is approximately 800°C. [123] Molten

Table 25, Vapor Pressures over Solid Germanium Monosulfide.

Method of Determination	Temperature Range °C	Vapor Pressure, log P mm Hg	Year	Literature Source
Knudsen's Effusion	305—336	$-\dfrac{8643}{T} + 11,234$	1955	[126]
same	347—376	$-\dfrac{8848}{T} + 11,715$	1955	[126]
Transport (in Helium)	400—600	$-\dfrac{6526}{T} + 9,07$	1956	[127]
Knudsen's Effusion	338—399	$-\dfrac{9591}{T} + 12,357$	1956	[128]
same	300—500	$-\dfrac{8350}{T} + 10,78$	1957	[129]
Transport (in Nitrogen)	525—615	$-\dfrac{7597}{T} + 10,05$	1958	[124]
Knudsen's Effusion	433—596	$-\dfrac{6966}{T} + 9,10$	1960	[130]
Langmuir's Effusion	400—550	$-\dfrac{8160}{T} + 10,65$	1961	[131]

germanium disulfide is a transparent, mobile liquid of light-brown color, which on cooling forms an amber glass with a density of 5.81 g/cm^2. [4] This product is poorly wetted by water and is stable toward concentrated acids, but dissolves readily in concentrated caustic alkalis and in aqueous ammonia. Multiple treatment of germanium disulfide with nitric acid or hydrogen peroxide results in the formation of germanium dioxide.

The equilibrium vapor pressure over solid germanium disulfide has been studied by several authors. Table 26 shows the results of these investigations.

The results obtained by Langmuir's effusion method proved to be low as compared to other data, as will be apparent below:

Vapor pressure over germanium disulfide at 500°C

3.3x10^{-5} 1.3x10^{-2} 1.7x10^{-2} 2.0x10^{-1} 4.0x10^{-3}

From the data of

(127)   (138)   (135)   (137)   (131)

Table 26, Vapor Pressure Over Solid Germanium Disulfide.

Method of Determination	Temperature Range, °C	Vapor Pressure, log P mm Hg	Year	Literature Source
Langmuir's Effusion	425—550	$-\dfrac{9931}{T} + 8{,}37$	1956	[127]
Knudsen's Effusion	420—490	$-\dfrac{11822}{T} + 13{,}423$	1956	[138]
Knudsen's Effusion	460—650	$-\dfrac{10970}{T} + 12{,}44$	1957	[135]
Transport (in Argon)	500—800	$-\dfrac{9030}{T} + 43{,}97 \times \lg T - 139{,}19$	1960	[137]
Langmuir's Effusion	550—675	$-\dfrac{10680}{T} + 11{,}4$	1961	[131]

Langmuir's method gives low results if Langmuir's coefficient characterizing the evaporation of a given substance is not equal to unity, and this was not taken into consideration in the calculations of.[12] The results obtained by the transport method[137] proved to be somewhat high, apparently because of the influence of the thermal diffusion of the vapor at low gas flow rates. Therefore, the results obtained by Knudsen's effusion method in ref.[135,138] are more reliable.

When germanium disulfide is heated in a vacuum or in a neutral atmosphere to 460-650°C, the following processes are likely to occur:

$$GeS_2(s) \longrightarrow GeS_2(g); \qquad (a)$$
$$2GeS_2(s) \longrightarrow 2GeS(g) + S_2(g); \qquad (b)$$
$$2GeS(g) \longrightarrow 2Ge(s) + S_2(g); \qquad (c)$$
$$GeS_2(s) \longrightarrow Ge(s) + S_2(g). \qquad (d)$$

Reaction (b) forms gaseous germanium monosulfide, since, according to the data cited above, the vapor pressure of the monosulfide at these temperatures

is hundreds of times greater than the equilibrium
vapor pressure over germanium disulfide. [135] According to the data of, [132] a determination of the
equilibrium pressure of sulfur at 650°C for reaction
(b) gives a value which is somewhat higher than
10^{-2} mm Hg, and for (c), 10^{-5} mm Hg. It can
therefore be assumed that reactions (b) and (c)
play an insignificant part at $460-650^\circ$C. The dissociation of germanium disulfide according to reaction (d) is still less probable in this temperature
range, since, according to A. A. Baikov's well-
known principle of the stepwise nature of dissociation,
oxidation, and reduction processes, this reaction
proceeds successively via (b) and (c). In view
of the above, the calculation of the equilibrium vapor
pressure from the experimental data obtained in the
range of $460-650^\circ$C was performed by assuming the
existence of only germanium disulfide molecules in
the vapor. [135] Figure 50 shows straight lines
representing the equilibrium pressures for reactions
(a) and (b). Extrapolation of these straight lines

shows that the disulfide dissociates completely in accordance with reaction (b) only above 800°C.

The vapor pressure of germanium disulfide in the range of $460-650^{\circ}$C is described by the equation

$$\log P \text{ (mm Hg)} = -\frac{10970}{T} + 12.44,$$

whence the change in free energy on sublimation of germanium disulfide is equal to

$$\Delta F = 50100 - 43.7T.$$

The changes in enthalpy and entropy on sublimation of germanium disulfide are equal respectively to: $\Delta H_T = 50100$ cal/mole and $\Delta S_T = 43.7$ cal/mole deg. The conditional boiling point of germanium disulfide, calculated without taking the dissociation of the disulfide into account, is 904°C.

An experimental determination of the degree of dissociation of germanium disulfide, made by comparing the saturation with vapors of various gases, has shown that at 700°C the degree of dis-

sociation of germanium disulfide into the monosulfide
and sulfur does not exceed 15%.[137] This supports
the hypothesis that germanium disulfide sublimes
without decomposition at 460-650°C.

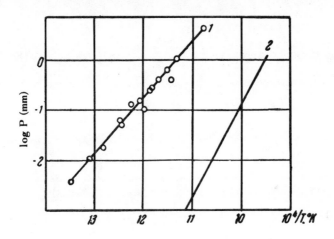

Fig. 50, Equilibrium Pressure Over Germanium Disulfide as a Function of Temperature:

1—Equilibrium Pressure; 2—Pressure of Dissociation of Germanium Disulfide According to Reaction (b)

In,[137] measurements were made of the saturated
vapor pressure over solid germanium disulfide by

the transport method in argon and in a mixture consisting of 90% argon and 10% hydrogen. The results obtained as well as the values of the constants of dissociation of the disulfide into germanium monosulfide and sulfur are listed in Table 27.

The saturated vapor pressure of germanium disulfide rises sharply when hydrogen is present in the gaseous mixture. This indicates an appreciable reduction of germanium disulfide to the monosulfide, which is highly volatile. In, [137] this is explained by the reaction of hydrogen with sulfur, one of the dissociation products of germanium disulfide, which leads to a shift in the equilibrium of the dissociation process. The temperature dependence of the constant of dissociation of germanium disulfide into the monosulfide and sulfur is given by the equation[137]

$$\log K_{GeS_2} \text{ (tech. atm.}^3) = -\frac{35470}{T} + 30.10.$$

Table 27, Saturated Vapor Pressure and Dissociation Constants of Germanium Disulfide.

Temperature °C	Saturated Vapor Pressure of GeS$_2$, mm Hg		$K_{GeS_2} = P^2_{GeS} \cdot P_{S_2}$ (Tech. Atm.^{3})
	In Argon	In Mixture of 90% Ar + 10% H$_2$	
500	0,347	1,796	$1,84 \cdot 10^{-16}$
550	0,865	5,325	$9,75 \cdot 10^{-14}$
600	2,808	14,384	$2,58 \cdot 10^{-11}$
650	10,057	35,336	$5,12 \cdot 10^{-9}$
700	32,834	60,337	$2,39 \cdot 10^{-7}$
750	94,144	—	—
800	320,150	—	—

The rate of volatilization of germanium disulfide in a vacuum, determined thermogravimetrically, increases sharply with rising temperature[131] (Figure 51). Experiments have shown that the sublimation rate of powdered germanium disulfide having grains less than 0.3 mm in size is directly proportional to the surface of evaporation and independent of the degree of pulverization. At 675°C, the sublimation rate reaches 706 kg/m^2 day.

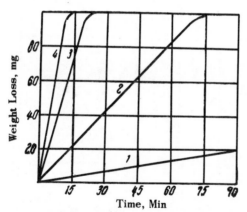

Fig. 51, Temperature Dependence of the Volatilization Rate of Germanium Disulfide:

1—at 550°C; 2—600°C; 3—650°C; 4—675°C

Sublimation of germanium disulfide in a stream of nitrogen with a continuous and smooth rise in temperature showed that the rate of the process increases rapidly above 720-730°C. [134]

The oxidation of germanium disulfide by oxygen is discussed in several studies. [82, 133, 134 and 139] In the study of, [82] in which air was circulated in the apparatus and the sulfur dioxide formed was frozen out with liquid nitrogen, it was shown that the oxidation rate of the disulfide increased sharply above 500°C.

Thermodynamic calculations of the processes of oxidation of germanium disulfide to the dioxide and sulfate were carried out. [139] Both processes are probable in the interval of 25-788°C. An appreciable increase in the oxidation rate takes place at 380-435°C.

Interesting data on the oxidation of germanium disulfide were obtained in. [133, 134] Use of the thermogravimetric method made it possible to follow

the weight loss of the sample continuously. The
residues from the oxidation of the disulfide were
subjected to chemical and x-ray structural analyses.
The phase composition of the products obtained 20,
40 and 60 minutes after the start of the oxidation of
germanium disulfide at various temperatures is
shown in Table 28.

As is evident from Figure 52, the maximum content of germanic sulfate is observed at 500-530°C.
Above these temperatures, the sulfate begins to
decompose on prolonged heating. Up to 625°C, the
sulfate and oxide are formed. The oxidation of
germanium disulfide above 625°C proceeds with the
formation of germanium dioxide only. Indeed, at
530-570°C, the content of $Ge(SO_4)_2$ and of the oxidation products does not exceed 30%. At 625°C, the
amount of sulfate in the oxidation products is only
1-2%, and after 40 min of exposure to these conditions, the sulfate decomposes completely. Most
of the oxidation in the layer at 440-720°C occurs in

the first 10-20 min. Subsequently, oxidation under
these conditions either proceeds very slowly or
virtually comes to a halt. This is explained by the
fact that the disulfide present on the surface becomes covered with an oxidation product (sulfate or
oxide) which is stable under these conditions; as a
result, the process acquires a diffusional character.

The literature contains practically no data on the
thermodynamic constants of germanium disulfide.

Germanium Sulfide Ge_2S_3

In ref. [135] it was noted that the decrease in the
equilibrium pressure over solid germanium disulfide
above 650°C may be caused by the formation of a
solid solution in germanium disulfide of the monosulfide formed as a result of the dissociation.
Fusion of this product was observed at 728°C.

A study of the condensates obtained after heating
germanium disulfide in a stream of nitrogen showed
that one of the products corresponded in chemical

Table 28, Phase Composition of the Products of Oxidation of Germanium Disulfide Under Isothermal Conditions, %.

Oxidation Temperature °C	Time Elapsed From the Start of Oxidation, min.								
	20			40			60		
	GeS_2	GeO_2	$Ge(SO_4)_2$	GeS_2	GeO_2	$(GeSO_4)_2$	GeS_2	GeO_2	$Ge(SO_4)_2$
440	58,2	23,4	18,4	58,8	29,7	11,5	57,8	30,6	11,6
455	73,6	14,2	12,2	46,2	35,1	18,7	37,4	46,6	16,0
500	58,5	18,1	23,4	53,4	20,0	26,6	50,0	21,9	28,1
530	68,6	12,2	19,2	61,4	12,2	26,4	57,1	12,5	30,4
570	57,7	17,2	25,1	64,8	18,0	17,2	63,6	18,1	18,3
625	71,9	26,9	1,2	64,7	32,9	2,4	62,6	37,4	—
675	78,5	21,5	—	74,5	25,5	—	70,5	29,5	—
690	80,5	19,5	—	79,2	20,8	—	77,9	22,1	—

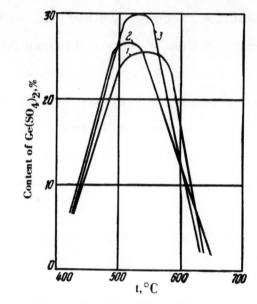

Fig. 52, Temperature Dependence of
$Ge(SO_4)_2$ Content in the Products of

Oxidation of Germanium Disulfide in
a Stream of Air:

1–20 min After Start of Experiment; 2–Same,
40 min; 3–Same, 60 min.

composition to the formula Ge_2S_3.[124] This was a
loose, yellowish-brown powder. Under the microscope, the fine crystals had many pores, and cracks
could be discerned. The x-ray diffraction pattern
showed no distinct lines which would permit the calculation of the lattice. Only a few faint lines were
observed whose position was different from that of
the lines of germanium monosulfide or disulfide.
Digermanium trisulfide is insoluble in all acids,
including aqua regia, and also in carbon disulfide.
It dissolves readily in an aqueous solution of ammonia
and can be oxidized with 3% hydrogen peroxide to
germanium dioxide at room temperature.

These data do not constitute a direct proof of the
existence of digermanium trisulfide. Another fact
which is cited to dispute its existence is the valence
of germanium, which is usually 2 or 4 in chemical
compounds.

Complex Sulfides of Germanium

The reaction of silver nitrate with germanium sulfide in a solution of sodium·sulfide leads to the formation of a salt of the composition $GeS_2 \cdot 4Ag_2S$.[4]

A complex copper-germanium sulfide of the composition $CuS \cdot GeS_2$ precipitates from an equimolar solution of copper and germanium in 4 N hydrochloric acid in the presence of a two- or threefold excess of the precipitant, sodium sulfide.[140]

The oxidation of the complex sulfide proceeds with the evolution of sulfur dioxide and with the formation of oxides. The rate of oxidation by atmospheric oxygen increases sharply at temperatures above $450-500°C$.[82]

Germanium disulfide precipitates completely from solutions whose acidity is no less than 4-6 N in hydrochloric acid. The precipitation of germanium as the disulfide from solutions of various acidities and the coprecipitation with sulfides of trivalent and pentavalent arsenic were studied. [141] The experiments showed that a virtually complete precipitation of germanium disulfide at concentrations of the latter of 20-50 mg/l in sulfuric and hydrochloric acid solutions takes place at acidities as low as 1.5 N and above.

When germanium coprecipitates with arsenic trisulfide from 0.2 N solutions of sulfuric acid and at a germanium concentration of 5 to 200 mg/l, the coprecipitation proceeds only to the extent of 12-58%. In the case of pentavalent arsenic, a complete coprecipitation of germanium is achieved at an atomic ratio of sulfur to arsenic of 4:1 and a pH of the solution less than 2. The coprecipitation of germanium from solutions of low acidity, where one cannot expect the precipitation of pure germanium disulfide, may be explained by the adsorption of germanium on the negatively charged precipitate of arsenic sulfide.

Germanium Selenides and Tellurides

Germanium selenides GeSe and $GeSe_2$ have been obtained at $500^\circ C$. They are insoluble in alkalis and are oxidized to GeO_2 by nitric acid.[2] The selenides and tellurides can be dissolved in aqua regia.[142] Data on the saturated vapor pressure over solid germanium selenide and telluride were obtained by Knudsen's effusion method.[142] The dissociation energy of GeSe is equal to 100 ± 15 kcal/mole, and that of GeTe, 80 ± 15 kcal/mole. Preliminary experiments on the sublimation of germanium selenide and telluride on heating at about 10^{-4} mm Hg have shown that germanium selenide vaporizes appreciably at $520-560^\circ C$, and the telluride does so at $600-640^\circ C$. The composition of the solid does not change on sublimation. For this reason, Knudsen's method is fully applicable. The results obtained are described by the equations for GeSe in the range of $414-596^\circ C$:

$$\log P \text{ (mm Hg)} = -\frac{9384}{T} + 10.728,$$

and for GeTe in the range of 437-606°C:

$$\log P \text{ (mm Hg) } = -\frac{10058}{T} + 11.314.$$

Hence, the heat of sublimation of germanium selenide is equal to 42.9$\pm$3.0 kcal/mole, and that of the telluride, 45.8$\pm$3.0 kcal/mole.

7. GERMANIUM HALIDES

Simple Halides of Divalent Germanium

Germanium difluoride is obtained as a white sublimate from the reaction between germanium tetrafluoride vapors and germanium.[143] It has an orthorhombic lattice with parameters a = 3.30 Å, b = 5.17 Å and c = 4.17 Å. The difluoride has strong reducing properties.

Germanium difluoride can be obtained in similar fashion.[4] Attempts to study this compound by reducing germanium tetrachloride were unsuccessful. On heating to 75°C, the dichloride begins to decompose. At 460°C, the disproportionation of

the dichloride into free germanium and the tetrachloride takes place exclusively. The reaction of
germanium dichloride with dry oxygen leads to the
formation of germanium dioxide and germanium
tetrachloride:

$$2GeCl_2 + O_2 \longrightarrow GeO_2 + GeCl_4.$$

Germanium dichloride is hydrolyzed by water. It
is partially oxidized when it comes in contact with
moist oxygen. However, water vapor acts more
strongly that oxygen, so that the reaction

$$GeCl_2 + 2H_2O \longrightarrow Ge(OH)_2 + 2HCl$$

takes place as the first stage. Hydrogen chloride
immediately reacts with the remaining germanium
dichloride to form trichlorogermane, which is
carried off by the stream of oxygen.

When acted upon by concentrated hydrochloric acid,
germanium dichloride converts into a white solid
substance which readily dissolves in acid. Free
chlorine oxidizes germanium dichloride to the

tetrachloride. The reaction with bromine forms a
colorless liquid consisting of a mixture of germanium
tetrachloride and tetrabromide and including traces
of the mixed halide $GeBr_2Cl_2$. The reaction of
hydrogen sulfide with germanium disulfide leads to
the formation of germanium sulfide even at room
temperature. [4]

Germanium dichloride forms two types of salts
with alkaloids, for example, with quinine and
pyrocarpin. [4] Like germanium dibromide solutions,
germanium dichloride solutions reduce salts of gold
and silver, potassium permanganate, and indigo
carmine.

Germanium dibromide is formed as a by-product
in the preparation of tribromogermane by the action
of hydrogen bromide on heated germanium powder.
It is a colorless crystalline substance. Rapid
crystallization produces fine lustrous flakes, and
slow crystallization forms acicular crystals. Germanium dibromide is sparingly soluble in benzene,

toluene, and other hydrocarbons. It dissolves in alcohol and acetone to form colorless solutions which are strong reductants.

Heating of germanium dibromide produces the tetrabromide and free germanium. In water, germanium dibromide forms yellow germanous hydroxide. Germanium dibromide absorbs bromine with the evolution of heat and the formation of germanium tetrabromide. By reacting with hydrogen bromide, the dibromide forms tribromogermane.

Germanium diiodide is obtained from germanium tetraiodide by reduction with hypophosphorous acid according to the reaction

$$GeI_4 + H_2O + H_3PO_2 \rightarrow GeI_2 + 2HI + H_3PO_3.$$

The diiodie is obtained from germanium dioxide as follows: germanium dioxide is dissolved in a concentrated solution of sodium hydroxide, and a 6 N solution of hydrochloric is added until the precipitated germanium dioxide dissolves completely. So–

lutions of concentrated hydrochloric acid and 50%
hypophosphorous acid are added in the cold, then
the solution is heated for 5-6 hours at 100°C in an
atmosphere of carbon dioxide. After cooling by the
addition of an ammonia solution, germanous
hydroxide precipitates. The precipitate is filtered
off in a nitrogen atmosphere and is transferred in
the moist state in to a solution of hydriodic acid
which is kept boiling. Germanium tetraiodide is
removed from the precipitate of the filtered germanous iodide by heating in a vacuum at 100°C. [144]

X-ray structural analysis has shown that germanium diiodide has a CdI_2-type lattice with constants
a = 4.249 Å and c = 6.833 Å.

There are also other methods of preparing germanium diiodide, for instance, treatment of germanium dichloride with potassium iodide, dissolution of germanium monoxide in concentrated
hydriodic acid, etc. [4]

Germanium diiodide is a yellow solid insoluble in hydrocarbons and sparingly soluble in chloroform and carbon tetrachloride. Germanium diiodide oxidizes in air to form germanium dioxide. It does not melt on heating, but rapidly oxidizes in air at 210°C to form a mixture of germanium dioxide and germanium tetraiodide. Decomposition with the formation of tetraiodide and free germanium occur at higher temperatures. The heat of oxidation of germanous iodide was determined by a direct and an indirect method.[144]

Direct oxidation with hypochlorous acid according to the reaction

$$GeI_2 (s) + I_3^- + 3H_2O \longrightarrow H_2GeO_3 (aq) + 4H^+ + 5I^-$$

gave the value $\Delta H_{298} = 26.0 \pm 1.0$ kcal/mole. An indirect determination, which took into account the heat of the hydration $H_2O + GeO_2 (s) \rightarrow H_2GeO_3 (aq)$, where $\Delta H^{\circ}_{288} = 3.3$ kcal/mole, and involved the use of the equation

$$GeI_2(s) + 2H_2O + I_3^- \longrightarrow GeO_2(s) + 4H^+ + 5I^-$$

gave the value $\Delta H_{298} = -29.3 \pm 1.4$ kcal/mole.

The enthalpy change under standard conditions for the disproportionation of germanium diiodide according to the reaction

$$2GeI_2(s) \longrightarrow Ge(s) + GeI_4$$

is equal to 30.1 kcal/mole. [80] The vapor pressure of germanium diiodide at 284°C is 0.1 mm Hg. [145]

Simple Halides of Tetravalent Germanium

Germanium tetrafluoride may be obtained in yields up to 87% by heating barium hexafluogermanate $BaGeF_6^-$. [4] The product is purified by distillation. The reaction is carried out in quartz apparatus.

At room temperature, germanium tetrafluoride is a colorless gas. It fumes heavily in air and has a pungent odor of garlic. On cooling with liquid air, the tetrafluoride forms a crystalline mass. It sublimes on heating without melting at atmospheric pressure. At a vapor pressure of 3032 mm Hg, germanium tetrafluoride melts at -15°C. Figure 53 shows the vapor pressures of germanium tetrahalides.[104] The halides are highly volatile. The values of the heat capacity and entropy change smoothly in the series of germanium tetrahalides (Table 29).[145]

When germanium tetrafluoride is bubbled through water, the gas is quickly absorbed with the evolution of a considerable amount of heat. A solution of fluo-germanic acid is thus formed:

$$3GeF_4 + 2H_2O \longrightarrow GeO_2 + 2H_2GeF_6.$$

Further saturation precipitates gelatinous germanic hydroxide. At room temperature, germanium tetrafloride does not appreciably react with glass, but attacks it in the presence of moisture. At temperatures below 700°C, it does not attack quartz. No dissociation is observed when the tetrafluoride is heated to 1000°C.

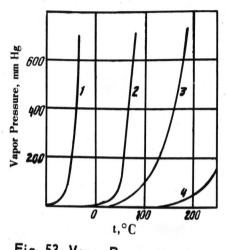

Fig. 53, Vapor Pressures of
Germanium Tetrahalides:
1–GeF$_4$; 2–Ge Cl$_4$;3–GeBr$_4$;
4–GeI$_4$.

Table 29, Heat Capacities and Entropies
of Gaseous Germanium Tetrahalides at
298°K.

Halide	C_p, kcal/mole deg	kcal/mole deg
GeFe$_4$	19,57	72,51
GeCl$_4$	22,97	83,05
GeBr$_4$	24,34	94,77
GeI$_4$	25,10	107,90

Germanium tetrachloride is obtained by the action of chlorine on metallic germanium or of hydrogen chloride on germanium dioxide. [4, 147] The rate of the reaction between chlorine and single-crystal germanium was studied in the range of 175-260°C at chlorine pressures up to 130 mm Hg. [146] The temperature dependence of the reaction rate obeys the equation

$$v = 10^{27 \pm 1} \cdot e^{\dfrac{-25000 \pm 1000}{RT}} \text{ molecules/cm}^2 \text{ sec.}$$

A study of the reaction between germanium powder and gaseous chlorine at 260-310°C showed that the process lasts several hours (when the germanium sample weighs 200 g, 34.5 hours). The yield was in excess of 92%. [147]

Germanium tetrachloride is a colorless mobile liquid which boils at 83.1°C and solidifies at -49.5°C; its density at 25°C is 1.874 g/cm^3. [4] According to other data, the boiling point is 82.5°C. [147] The tetrachloride fumes in air and is hydrolyzed by water. It does not dissolve in con-

centrated hydrochloric and does not react with concentrated sulfuric acid. It is soluble in absolute
ethanol, carbon disulfide, benzene, chloroform,
and ethyl ether. Germanium tetrachloride mixes
well with sulfur dioxide and partially with liquid
phosphine.

In preparing films of pure germanium, use is
made of the reduction of germanium tetrachloride in
the gas phase followed by crystallization of germanium. The reduction is carried out with hydrogen.
The yield of germanium is very low, but the films
formed have a high degree of purity, which permits
their use in photoresistances, photocells, etc. The
simultaneous reduction of certain other compounds
with germanium chloride produces doped films with
predetermined semiconducting characteristics.
The reduction proceeds according to the reaction

$$GeCl_4 + 2H_2 \rightarrow Ge + 4HCl.$$

The substrates used for the deposition of the film
are graphite, quartz, tungsten, or molybdenum.

The reaction time necessary for the formation of
films 20-80 mμ thick is 15-60 min. As was shown
experimentally, the highest yield of germanium is
observed at 900°C. [148] In order to obtain dense
films of the required thickness, it is necessary to
supply hydrogen in quantities 90-100 times greater
than the stoichiometric amounts.

As the reduction temperature rises, the concentration of germanium vapor in the reaction zone increases because of a shift of the reaction equilibrium
to the right and an increase in the reaction rate. It
would seem that this should result in a supersaturation of germanium and the formation of finer crystals.
However, as the temperature rises, the vapor pressure of germanium increases, i.e., the degree of
supersaturation decreases, promoting the growth of
coarser crystals.

The reaction between germanium tetrachloride and
a 20:80 copper-silicon alloy was studied in the range
of 300-500°C. [147] Results of the fractionation of

the reaction products are shown in Table 30.

At 400-500°C, silicon tetrachloride is formed, and metallic germanium deposits on the surface of the alloy as a finely divided powder.

Investigations of the reaction of germanium tetrachloride with calcium oxide showed that the process begins above 395°C.[149] The change in the weight of the solid sample is used to study the mechanism of the process (Figure 54), which takes place in steps:

above 395°C,

$$4CaO + GeCl_4 \longrightarrow Ca_2GeO_4 + 2CaCl_2;$$

above 595°C,

$$3CaO + GeCl_4 \longrightarrow CaGeO_3 + 2CaCl_2;$$

and above 650°C,

$$5CaO + 2GeCl_4 \longrightarrow CaGe_2O_5 + 4CaCl_2.$$

As a whole, the transformations occur in the following sequence:

$$GeCl_4 + 4CaO \rightarrow Ca_2GeO_4 + 2CaCl_2;$$

$$3Ca_2GeO_4 + GeCl_4 \rightarrow 4CaGeO_3 + 2CaCl_2;$$

$$5CaGeO_3 + GeCl_4 \rightarrow 3CaGe_2O_5 + 2CaCl_2.$$

As was shown above, germanium tetrachloride dissolves well in nonpolar organic solvents.

It is known that germanium can be extracted almost completely with carbon tetrachloride from 9-12 N solutions of hydrochloric acid; only trivalent arsenic and tetravalent osmium are extracted together with germanium. This has permitted an extensive use of this extraction in the analytical chemistry of germanium. Germanium is thought to be extracted in the form of a tetravalent compound. The reextraction of germanium with water is relatively easy.

The solubility of germanium tetrachloride in 7 N hydrochloric acid at $20^{\circ}C$ may reach 37 g/l. This high solubility may be explained by a partial hydrolysis

of germanium tetrachloride. As the concentration of
hydrochloric acid changes, the solubility decreases
accordingly. (150)

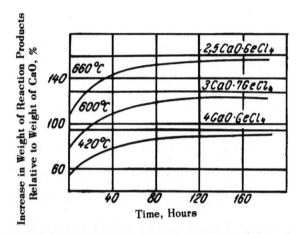

Fig. 54, Change in the Weight of Solid Sample
During Reaction of Calcium Oxide with Germanium Tetrachloride.

Experiments have been carried out involving the
extraction of germanium tetrachloride with a mixture
of hydrocarbons which constituted the kerosene
fraction of petroleum and contained 50.45% un-

saturated, 26.60% aromatic and 23.00% naphthene
hydrocarbons. [150] It had been established earlier
that hydrocarbons of different categories extract
germanium tetrachloride equally well. The distribution coefficient of germanium increases with
rising temperature. This also happens when the
concentration of germanium in the system is increased.

The fact that the distribution coefficient for such
solvents as hydrocarbons, tributyl phosphate,
dichlorodiethyl alcohol, benzene, and chloroform has
almost the same value indicates that germanium is
extracted in the form of the same compound, namely,
the tetrachloride.

On the basis of experiments on the solubility of germanium tetrachloride in hydrocarbons and hydrochloric acid, and from the data on the vapor pressure
of germanium tetrachloride over its solutions, the
corresponding distribution coefficients of germanium
were calculated. [150] The results are given in
Table 31.

Table 31, Coefficients of Distribution of Germanium Between Hydrocarbons and Hydrochloric Acid Solutions.

Hydrochloric Acid Concentration, g—eq/l	Distribution Coefficients of Germanium		
	From Solubility	From Vapor Pressure	Experimental Data
7,0	95	20	35
8,5	459	—	380
8,8	840	480	680
9,0	1300	—	1200
11,5	5500	4850	4900

Table 30, Fractionation Products.

Fraction No.	Boiling Temperature, °C	Yield of Fraction, %, at Temperatures, °C, of		
		300—320	400	500
1	56—58	0,8	26,5	42,0
2	58—80	0,9	1,3	1,2
3	80—83	95,3	60,2	56,0
4	Above 83.	1,0	2,1	1,8

The increase in the distribution coefficient associated with a decrease in the solubility of germanium
tetrachloride and a rising concentration of hydrochloric acid indicates that the extractability of germanium, like its solubility, is determined by the
extent of hydrolysis of its tetrachloride. In 9-12 N
hydrochloric acid, when germanium tetrachloride is
hydrolyzed to a small extent, the values of the distribution coefficients of germanium reach their
maximum values.

Figure 55 shows a phase diagram of the $GeCl_4$ -
$AsCl_3$ system.[104] The boiling points of germanium
tetrachloride and arsenic tetrachloride are close to
each other. Therefore, in the processes of distillation of germanium, use is made of oxidizing agents
which make it possible to convert the arsenic to the
pentavalent state. It is necessary to carry out
repeated distillations in order to obtain pure germanium tetrachloride. Figure 56 shows the dependence of the resistivity of germanium on the type

and number of repeated distillations of the
tetrachloride. [104]

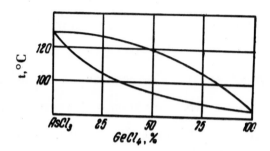

Fig. 55, Phase Diagram of The System
$$GeCl_4 - AsCl_3$$

A study of the influence of hydrochloric acid concentration on the volatility of germanium tetrachloride in the range of 83-108.5°C showed that the
concentration of the tetrachloride in the vapor phase
reaches the value of its concentration in the liquid
phase at a hydrochloric acid content of 17%. [151]
As the hydrochloric acid concentration rises, the
equilibrium concentration of germanium tetrachloride
in the vapor phase decreases.

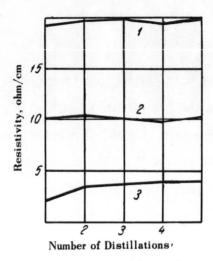

Fig. 56, Dependence of the Resistivity of Germanium on the Type and Number of Repeated Distillations:

1—Widmer column; 2—Ordinary column; 3—no column.

Dry gaseous ammonia reacts with germanium tetrachloride to form a light, loose white powder of the composition $GeCl_4 \cdot 6NH_3$. The powder is a mixture of one molecule of germanium imide $Ge(NH_2)_2$ and four molecules of ammonium chloride.[4] A similar reaction takes place when excess ethylamine yields a mixture of diethylgermanium

diamide $Ge(N(C_2H_5)_2)_2$ and ethylamine hydrochloride
in the proportion of 1:4.

Aniline reacts with germanium tetrachloride to
form a solid of the composition $GeCl_4 \cdot 4C_6H_5NH_2.$[4]
This substance reacting with hydrochloric acid
forms a compound which includes aniline hydrochloride. The part which is soluble in ether is the
diimide hydrochloride $Ge(NC_6H_5 \cdot HCl)_2.$

Germanium tetrachloride reacts with piperidine:

$$GeCl_4 + 8C_5H_{10}NH \rightarrow Ge(NC_5H_{10})_4 +$$
$$4C_5H_{10}NH \cdot HCl;$$

the reaction forms a stable compound. [4]

Germanium tetrabromide is formed when bromine
vapors are passed over germanium or when hydrobromic acid reacts with germanium dioxide. [4] The
latter method is more efficient and gives the products
in yields up to 90%.

Germanium tetrabromide melts at 26.1°C. In the liquid state, it is a colorless, mobile liquid. The density at 29°C is 3.13 g/cm^3. The refractive index is 1.6269. The vapor pressure at 18.35°C is 3.6 mm Hg and at 180.39°C, 649.8 mm Hg. [4] German-ium tetrabromide dissolves in ethyl alcohol, carbon tetrachloride, benzene, and ether. In acetone, ger-manium tetrabromide decomposes slowly with the evolution of bromine. It hydrolyzes rapidly in water with the formation and evolution of germanium dioxide. In aqueous solutions of potassium hydroxide, hydro-lysis is more vigorous, and the germanium dioxide thus produced dissolves. Germanium tetrabromide reacts violently with concentrated nitric acid, and nitrogen oxides are evolved. It does not react to any appreciable extent with concentrated sulfuric acid.

Germanium tetraiodide is obtained by treating ger-manium dioxide with 57% hydriodic acid acid. [4] The yield attains 85%. The tetraiodide is also formed by heating germanium in iodine vapor. It is stable in

air, but hydrolyzes slowly in water. The heat of
hydrolysis is 9.6 kcal/mole. [80] Concentrated sulfuric acid does not react with germanium tetraiodide;
it dissolves slowly in concentrated hydrochloric acid
at room temperature. Heating causes dissociation
into germanium diiodide and iodine. Germanium
tetraiodide can be partially reduced by hydrogen or
acetylene. Reaction with zinc in 25% sulfuric acid
causes the evolution of monogermane. The vapor
pressure of germanium tetraiodide at 284°C is 0.5
mm Hg. [145]

In studying the vapor pressure of germanium tetraiodide, use was made of the method of a stream of
saturated gas. [145] Argon was passed over crystals
of germanium tetraiodide placed in a horizontal
glass tube and heated to a certain temperature. The
vapor pressure was determined from the weight of the
condensed germanium tetraiodide, assuming that the
gas had been completely saturated. The results of
the measurements are shown in Table 32.

Table 32, Vapor Pressure of Germanium Tetraiodide.

Temperature, °K	Supply Rate of Argon, mole/min	Pressure, tech. atm.	
		In Tube	Of Germanium Iodide
393	$0,746 \cdot 10^{-3}$	0,999	$8,2 \cdot 10^{-4}$
393	$0,387 \cdot 10^{-3}$	1,007	$8,4 \cdot 10^{-4}$
393	$1,69 \cdot 10^{-3}$	1,008	$7,1 \cdot 10^{-4}$
393	0 (extrapolation)	—	$8,7 \cdot 10^{-4}$
408	$0,527 \cdot 10^{-3}$	1,010	$1,79 \cdot 10^{-3}$
379	$0,774 \cdot 10^{-3}$	1,000	$2,9 \cdot 10^{-4}$
373	$0,735 \cdot 10^{-3}$	1,002	$2,20 \cdot 10^{-4}$
353	$0,634 \cdot 10^{-3}$	0,999	$4,7 \cdot 10^{-5}$

As is evident from Table 32, the gas was saturated with iodine at a rate as low as 0.7×10^{-3} mole/min. The heat capacity of gaseous germanium tetraiodide at 25° is 25.1 cal/mole deg, and that of the solid compound, 33 cal/mole deg.

The change in free energy on sublimation of germanium tetraiodide is

$$\Delta F_T = 22500 + 8\,T \ln T - 90.8\,T,$$

whence

$$\Delta H_T = 22500 - 8T,$$
$$\Delta S_T = 82.8 - 8\ln T$$

or, for standard conditions,

$$\Delta H_{298} = 20.1 \text{ kcal/mole},$$
$$\Delta S_{298} = 37 \text{ cal/mole deg}.$$

Halogermanes

The existence of the following series of halogermanes is known: $HGeCl_3$, $HGeClBr_2$, $HGeCl_2Br$, $HGeBr_3$, H_2GeCl_2. [1]

When germanium dichloride is treated with hydrogen chloride, trichlorogermane forms with the evolution of heat:[4]

$$GeCl_2 + HCl \longrightarrow HGeCl_3.$$

Tribromogermane can be obtained in similar fashion. Trichlorogermane can also be obtained by the action of hydrogen chloride on germanium or germanium sulfide with heating. However, in this case the reaction product is a mixture of trichlorogermane and germanium tetrachloride.[4]

Trichlorogermane is a colorless mobile liquid with a density of 1.93 g/cm^3. It decomposes on heating to 140°C. It is postulated that hydrogen chloride and germanium dichloride are formed first; as the temperature rises, germanium dichloride slowly disproportionates to form germanium and germanium tetrachloride. Trichlorogermane becomes clouded in air, and this probably involves the following reactions:

$$2HGeCl_3 + O_2 \longrightarrow 2GeOCl_2 + 2HCl;$$

$$4HGeCl_3 + O_2 \longrightarrow 2GeCl_4 + 2GeCl_2 + 2H_2O.$$

Trichlorogermane in a mixture with germanium tetrachloride can be determined iodometrically. In this case, iodine reacts only with trichlorogermane:

$$HGeCl_3 + I_2 \longrightarrow GeICl_3 + HI.$$

The excess iodine is back-titrated with hyposulfite.[4] The reaction with bromine has a similar course.

In the electrolysis of trichlorogermane in hydrochloric acid solution, germanium dioxide forms at the anode, but germanium is not deposited on the cathode. This may be explained by assuming the existence of the ion $GeCl_3^-$, which forms at the anode. This ion is hydrolyzed by dilute hydrochloric acid.[4]

Treatment of trichlorogermane with silver oxide yields germanium oxychloride according to the reaction

$$2HGeCl_3 + 3Ag_2O \longrightarrow 2GeOCl_2 + 4Ag + 3AgCl + H_2O.$$

Germanium oxychloride is a transparent colorless liquid insoluble in organic and inorganic solvents;[4] it is readily hydrolyzed to the dioxide by water. On heating in air, it is converted into germanium dioxide.

Mixed Complex Halides

Germanium forms many complex halides. When two different germanium halides are mixed, displacement of the atoms of the different halogens occurs. However, the equilibrium between the reaction products is easily disturbed, and the mixed halides formed cannot be isolated in the pure state. Halo derivatives of organic compounds are used for the synthesis of mixed halides. [4] The existence of $GeFCl_3$, GeF_2Cl_2, GeF_3Cl, $GeClF_3$, $GeCl_3F$ is known. [1, 4]

All of these mixed germanium chlorofluorides are insufficiently stable and rearrange even at the temperature of solid carbon dioxide to form germanium tetrachloride and tetrafluoride. When these compounds are heated in contact with metallic copper, a rapid and occasionally explosive decomposition takes place. Germanium dichloride and difluoride are thus formed. [4]

Mixed chloride-bromide compounds of germanium also have a tendency to rearrange with the formation of pure chlorides and bromides. The reaction of trichlorogermane with iodine forms iodotrichlorogermane:

$$HGeCl_3 + I_2 \longrightarrow GeICl_3 + HI.$$

Compounds of germanium tetrachloride with amines - hydroxyquinoline, pyridine, and ethylenediamine - have been prepared. [152] The formulas suggested for these compounds are: $GeCl_4 \cdot 4C_2H_8N_2$, $GeCl_4 \cdot 2C_5H_5N$, $GeCl_4 \cdot 4C_9H_7NO$. These compounds are powders amorphous in appearance: the one with hydroxyquinoline is yellow, and the other two are white. They are readily hydrolyzed in water and are insoluble in common organic solvents.

The thermal decomposition of the compound $GeCl_4 \cdot 4C_9H_7NO$ or its heating in a solvent produced a compound of the composition $GeCl_4(C_9H_6NO)_2$. The reaction of $GeCl_2(C_9H_6NO)_2$ with dry gaseous ammonia at $100^\circ C$ yields the compound $GeCl_2(C_9H_6NO)_2 \cdot 2NH_3$.

A thermal analysis of the system $NOCl - GeCl_4$ was performed. [153] The compound $GeCl_2 \cdot 2NOCl$, stable at temperatures below $-62.3^\circ C$, was identified.

Halogermanes

When solutions of alkali metal fluorides are added to a solution of germanium dioxide in hydrofluoric acid, the corresponding hexafluogermanates can be obtained: Rb_2GeF_6, Cs_2GeF_6, K_2GeF_6, etc. [120]

Barium hexafluogermanate precipitates from a hydrofluoric acid solution (48.9% HF) of germanium dioxide when the theoretical amount of a saturated solution of barium chloride is added. On heating $(500^\circ C)$ in a quartz tube, the compound begins to

decompose with the formation of barium fluoride
and germanium tetrafluoride. At higher temperatures,
the decomposition is intensified. [4]

Germanium tetrafluoride decomposes rapidly in
water with the evolution of a considerable amount of
heat. A transparent solution with a strongly acidic
reaction is obtained. Its neutralization produces a
precipitate of potassium hexafluogermanate.

Cesium chloride precipitates a sparingly soluble
white microcrystalline precipitate of cesium tri-
chlorogermanyl $CsGeCl_3$ from a strong hydrochloric
acid solution. [4] The compound $RbGeCl_3$ can be
similarly obtained with rubidium chloride. Similar
compounds could not be obtained with lithium
chloride, sodium chloride or potassium chloride.
At $100^\circ C$ in an atmosphere of hydrogen chloride,
the cesium salt decomposes with the evolution of
germanium dichloride. At higher temperatures,
trichlorogermane is formed.

8. GERMANIUM HYDRIDES

Of major interest are compounds of germanium with hydrogen. These are essentially unstable and volatile compounds. Germanium monohydride $(GeH)_x$ is an amorphous brown solid.[1] It does not dissolve in common organic and inorganic solvents. Dilute or concentrated nitric acid and hydrogen peroxide quickly oxidize it to germanium dioxide. Germanium monohydride, washed with ether and dried, ignites when heated to $170°C$. On slow heating to $100°C$, decomposition evolving hydrogen takes place. Most of the hydrogen is evolved in the range of $100-200°C$; the process reaches completion at $500°C$. On detonation, germanium monohydride decomposes readily with the formation of germanium and hydrogen. The existence of germanium dihydride $(GeH_2)_2$ is known.[1]

At room temperature, monogermane GeH_4 is in the gaseous state. It decomposes on heating above $278-330°C$.[153] The decomposition isotherms are shown in Figure 57.

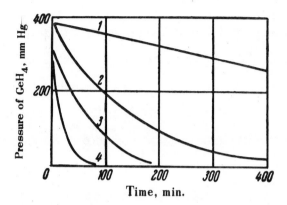

Fig. 57, Decomposition Isotherms of Germane.
1—at 278°C; 2—302°C; 3—314°C; 4—330°C.

Two reactions of formation of monogermane from germanium tetrachloride reacting with lithium aluminum hydrides have been studied. [154] Lithium aluminum hydride and lithium tri-tert-butoxyaluminum hydride were employed.

In the study of the first reaction, only 10-15% of monogermane and 85-90% of hydrogen were evolved. This is explained by the occurrence, in addition to the reaction

$$GeCl_4 + LiAlH_4 \longrightarrow GeH_4 + LiCl + AlCl_3,$$

of the following reactions forming germanium dichloride:

$$GeCl_4 + 2LiAlH_4 \longrightarrow GeCl_2 + H_2 + 2LiCl + 2AlH_3;$$

$$GeCl_4 + AlH_3 \longrightarrow GeCl_2 + H_2 + AlHCl_2.$$

The yield of monogermane resulting from the reaction of lithium tri-tertbutoxyaluminum hydride was 70-80% in 4-30 hours at room temperature. The following reaction took place

$$GeCl_4 + 4Li(t-BuO)_3AlH \longrightarrow GeH_4 + 4LiCl + 4(t-BuO)_3 \cdot Al.$$

The vapor pressure of monogermane at $-112°C$ is 180 mm Hg. [154]

The energy of the germanium-to-hydrogen bond in monogermane is close to 23 kcal/mole. [1] The heat capacity of liquid monogermane is about 15 cal/mole deg. Table 33 shows the physical constants of some germanium hydrides. [1, 155]

When magnesium germanide is added to a 10% aqueous solution of hydrochloric acid, a mixture of germanium hydride compounds is obtained. After the known germanes (GeH_4, Ge_2H_6 and Ge_3H_8) are driven off under a high vacuum at a temperature not above $21^{\circ}C$, a transparent colorless liquid remains. From the latter, Ge_4H_{10} and Ge_5H_{12} can be obtained by distillation in the range of 0 to $+20^{\circ}C$. [156]

Germanium hydrides are formed when zinc or magnesium acts on sulfuric acid solutions of germanium and also when germanium-magnesium alloys are dissolved in hydrochloric acid. [157]

Data on the vapor pressure of germanium hydrides are available. The vapor pressure of digermane Ge_2H_6 is given below: [1]

Temperature, $^{\circ}C$	-68.1	-63.0	-23.1	-10.2
Pressure, mm Hg.	6.4	8.5	86.5	152.7

Temperature, $^{\circ}C$	0.0	6.7	12.9	18.8
Pressure, mm Hg.	239.0	320.4	403.4	503.5

The decomposition of digermane proceeds at temperatures above $215^{\circ}C$, and that of trigermane, above $295^{\circ}C$. [155]

Tetragermane Ge_4H_{10} is a colorless mobile liquid which dissolves sparingly in benzene. Measurements of its vapor pressure in the range of 3-47°C led to the derivation of the relation [156]

$$\log P \text{ (mm Hg)} = -\frac{1714.6}{T} + 6.692.$$

At 100°C and above, it disproportionates by decomposing into monogermane and a higher hydride.

Ge_5H_{12} is a colorless oily liquid which can be distilled at 20°C under a high vacuum. Values of the vapor pressure measured in the range of 7-47°C obey the equation [156]

$$\log P \text{ (mm Hg)} = -\frac{1805.8}{T} + 6.449.$$

The reaction of disproportionation into monogermane and polygermane proceeds above 100°C, and into germanium and hydrogen, above 350°C.

In their chemical properties, germanium hydrides are reductants. They decompose when acted upon by oxidants such as nitric acid, potassium permanganate,

Table 33, Characteristics of Germanium Hydrides.

Compound	Fusion			Boiling		
	Temperature, °C	ΔH kcal/mole	ΔS cal/mole deg	Temperature, °C	ΔH kcal/mole deg	ΔS cal/mole deg
GeH_4	—165,8	199,7	1,86	—88,5	3,55	19,7
Ge_2H_6	—109,0	—	—	30,0	—	—
Ge_3H_8	—105,6	—	—	110,7	8,0	20,8
Ge_4H_{10}	—	—	—	177,0	9,65	21,45
Ge_5H_{12}	—	—	—	235,0	11,3	22,15

Table 34, Properties of Deuterogermanes.

Compound	Temperature, °C		Density		Heat of Vaporization, cal/mole
	Of Fusion	Of Boiling	g/cm³	at (°C)	
GeD_4	—166,2	—89,2	1,684	—160,5	3744
Ge_2D_6	—107,9	28,4	2,184	—106,4	6483
Ge_3D_8	—100,3	110,5	2,618	—99,9	7876

silver nitrate, and potassium dichromate. [157]

Experiments have shown the possibility of trapping volatile germanium hydrides in solutions of oxidants. Thus, up to 50-60% monogermane can be caught by an aqueous solution of potassium permanganate. [157]

Analogs of germanium hydrides are germanium deuterides. Some of their physical properties are shown in Table 34. [159]

The temperature dependences of the vapor pressures of germanium deuterides are given by the following equations: [159]

for GeD_4,

$$\log P \text{ (mm Hg)} = -\frac{3744}{4.575T} + 10.207;$$

for Ge_2D_6,

$$\log P \text{ (mm Hg)} = -\frac{6483}{4.575T} + 10.459;$$

for Ge_3D_8,

$$\log P \text{ (mm Hg)} = - \frac{7876}{4.575T} + 10.247.$$

The derivatives

$$CH_3GeH_3 \quad - \quad (CH_3)_2GeH_2 \quad - \quad (CH_3)_3GeH;$$

$$CH_3GeD_3 \quad - \quad (CH_3)_2GeD_2 \quad - \quad (CH_3)_3GeD;$$

$$C_2H_5GeH_3 \quad - \quad (C_2H_5)_2GeH_2 \quad - \quad (C_2H_5)_3GeH$$

and

$$C_2H_5GeD_3 \quad - \quad (C_2H_5)_2GeD_2 \quad - \quad (C_2H_5)_3GeD,$$

were obtained by reacting the corresponding alkylgermanium chlorides or alkylgermanium bromides
with lithium hydride or deuteride. The composition
and properties of these compounds are shown in
Table 35. [160]

9. COMPLEX COMPOUNDS OF GERMANIUM
AND ION EXCHANGE

Germanium has a pronounced tendency to form
complex compounds; in this it resembles silicon. An
analysis of the structure of complex compounds of

Table 35

Properties of Alkylgermanium Hydrides and Alkylgermanium Deuterides.

Compound	Boiling Point °C	Density, d_4^{20}, g/cm³	Refractive Index n_D^{20}
CH_3GeH_3	−23,5	—	—
CH_3GeD_3	−23,5	—	—
$(CH_3)_2GeH_2$	6,5	—	—
$(CH_3)_2GeD_2$	6,5	—	—
$(CH_3)_3GeH$	26,0	1,0128	1,3890
$(CH_3)_3GeD$	26,0	1,0207	1,3893
$C_2H_5GeH_3$	11,5	—	—
$C_2H_5GeD_3$	11,3	—	—
$(C_2H_5)_2GeH_2$	72,5	1,0378	1,4208
$(C_2H_5)_2GeD_2$	71,5	1,0525	1,4200
$(CH_3)_2 (C_2H_5)GeH$	62,0	1,0158	1,4090
$(CH_3)_2 (C_2H_5)GeD$	60,0	1,0262	1,4083

germanium tetrahalides shows that molecules of the
type of "outer" complexes may be formed through
the use of the 4d orbitals of germanium atoms. A
certain additional stabilization of the molecule of
the complex compound can also be achieved by the
formation of π bonds between the atoms of germanium and the addendum.

Complex compounds of germanium tetrachloride and
tetrabromide with the following amines were synthesized: 1, 10-phenanthroline, 2, 2'-dipyridyl, and
pyridine. [161] On heating, the complex compounds
decomposed with the formation of charred products
containing considerable amounts of germanium. It
is probable that during heating, germanium halides
act as catalysts in the decomposition of the organic
part of the molecules of the complex compound.

Germanium heteropoly compounds are widely
employed in analytical chemistry, and for this reason
a study of the structure and properties of these compounds is of interest.

It has been shown polarographically that in the range of pH 2.6-4.2, the anion $(GeW_{12}O_{40})^{4-}$ decomposes and converts completely into an anion containing 11 tungsten atoms. At higher pH values, the latter decomposes with the formation of germanates and tungstates.

The isothermal dehydration of crystal hydrates of germanotungstic acid and also their heating to $250^{\circ}C$ forms hydrates of both constant and variable compositions. Calculation of the values obtained for the content of water, based on the x-ray structural formula $H_4(GeW_{12}O_{40}) \cdot n-H_2O$, gives the following values of n: for hydrates of definite composition, 31, 24, 14 and 6; for phases of variable composition, from 17 to 14 for the first, from 14 to 12 for the second, and from 6 to 4 for the third phase. The water in these hydrates is water of crystallization.[162] The dehydration process is reversible and does not cause the decomposition of the heteropoly acid.

Germanomolybdic, germanovanadic, and germanotungstovanadic heteropoly acids have been obtained.
Just as in the case of silicon heteropoly acids,
soluble sodium and potassium salts and insoluble
salts of organic bases can be obtained. The
rubidium salt of the germanomolybdic heteropoly
acid of the composition $1.5Rb_2O \cdot GeO_2 \cdot 12 MoO_3$
$\cdot 4H_2O$ has been obtained. The acid cesium salt of
germanotungstic acid $Cs_3HGeW_{12}O_{40}$ is known.
Rubidium and cesium salts of germanomolybdovanadic
and germanotungstovanadic acid are known. The
ammonium, rubidium and cesium salts of all the
enumerated acids are sparingly soluble, and the
solubility decreases in the order ammonium -
rubidium - cesium. Thus, the solubility of ammonium
salts at $25^{\circ}C$ in sulfuric acid solutions is only a few
percent, that of rubidium salts, a few tenths of one
percent, and that of cesium salts, only a few
hundredths of one percent;[163] this is utilized in
analytical practice. As the concentration of sulfuric
acid increases, the solubility of the salts decreases.

The germanovanadomolybdic heteropoly acid $H_8(GeMo_{10}V_2O_{40})$ and germanomolybdic "blue," whose composition is unclear, are known. Electron-diffraction patterns of these compounds show that they have much in common from the standpoint of the arrangement of the rings and the sequence of line intensities, indicating a structural similarity. Indeed, they crystallize in the cubic system and have very close unit cell dimensions, 23.10 and 23.16 Å, respectively.[164]

The starting materials for the synthesis of germanotungstovanadic acid $H_8(Ge(W_2O_7)_5 \cdot V_2O_6) \cdot n\text{-}H_2O$ can be germanium, normal sodium tungstate, and sodium metavanadate.[165] The ratio germanium : tungsten : vanadium for the synthesis is 1:10:2, but the amount of vanadium employed is 4 times the stoichiometric amount.

An ion-exchange study of the complex compounds of germanium formed in concentrated solutions of mannitol, glycerol and ethanediol showed that they are obtained at high pH values. [166] The complex

compounds are formed at ratios of the components

of 3:1, 2:1 and 1:1. The stability of the compounds

decreases in the following order: mannitol >

glycerol > ethanediol. The adsorption of mannitol-

germanium and glycerol-germanium complexes on a

resin was also observed at low pH values. The

glycerol complexes decomposed immediately to

form polygermanates, but it is unclear whether this

occurs in solution or at the instant of the interaction

with the resin.

Complex compounds formed by the interaction of

germanic acid with tartrates, lactates, and mucates

were also studied by means of ion exchange. [167]

With tartaric acid, a 1:1 tartaric acid- germanium

complex is formed at a low concentration of tartaric

acid, and at higher concentration, the ratio of the

acid radicals becomes 3:2. With lactic acid, complex

compounds are formed with component ratios of 3:1,

2:1 and 1:1. Mucic acid forms complex compounds

with germanium as do lactic acid at low pH, tartaric

acid at intermediate pH, and complex compounds with higher alcohols at high pH values.

It has been noted that the complex-forming tendency of germanium increases in the following series of glycols: ethylene glycol - propylene glycol - butylene glycol. [172]

When germanic acid and pyrocatechol (H_2L) interact in aqueous solutions at a molar ratio $H_2GeO_3:H_2L = 1:2$, the complex compound $GeL_2 \cdot 2.5H_2O$ is formed which can be isolated in the crystalline form. The solubility of the compound in water is moderate. [173] When the compound is heated, a three-step decomposition takes place. At $200^\circ C$, one molecule of pyrocatechol splits off, a second molecule is detached at $300^\circ C$, and germanium hydroxide is formed which loses water on further heating to $800^\circ C$.

The formation of complexes by germanic acid with pyrogallol and with disodium pyrocatecholdisulfonate has been studied. [174]

The stability of oxyanion chelates of germanium depends considerably on the length of the carbon chain of the ligand[175] and increases in the series of complex compounds of germanium as follows: D-mannitol < D-dulcitol < D-sorbitol.

Complex formation between germanium and saccharides has been studied.[175] Compounds of germanium with mandelic and malic acid have been isolated in the crystalline state.[176]

Cyanide compounds of germanium have been described only in the alkaline form with one cyanide group $R_3Ge(CN)$.[177] Germanium tetracyanide decomposes quickly in water and alcohol. It is insoluble in benzene, ether, and anhydrous hydrocyanic acid. When $Ge(CH)_4$ is heated in air to 80-90°C, a dark-brown decomposition product is formed. The formation of germanium tetracyanide proceeds in accordance with the reaction

$$GeI_4 + 4AgCN \longrightarrow Ge(CN)_4 + 4AgI.$$

Germanium tetraiodide dissolves in absolute ether
and is introduced into a stream of nitrogen with AgCN.
From 16 to 20 moles of AgCN is consumed per mole
of GeI_4. After an exposure of 30 hours in a closed
stream at $80^{\circ}C$, the reaction goes to completion.

The existence of an iron carbonyl complex containing germanium, $(CH_3)_3Ge-N = C-Fe(CO)_4$, was
noted. [178]

In a study of the adsorption of germanate ions, the
forms in which germanium was present in solution
were determined. [168] Use was made of the
strongly basic anion exchanger Amberlite IRA-400
in the presence of Cl^- ions. Germanium is
adsorbed by this exchanger at pH 4-13. An adsorption
maximum was noted at pH 9.0-9.2. It was found that
in the range of pH = 6.9-9.4, pentagermanate ions
$Ge_5O_{11}^{2-}$ were adsorbed. A decrease in the
adsorption of germanium at lower pH values is due
to its adsorption in the form of monogermanate ions
$HGeO_3^-$ and GeO_3^{2-}. At pH values above 9.4, ger-

manate ions with a higher degree of polymerization
than that of $Ge_5O_{11}{}^{2-}$ are adsorbed.

In another study it was shown[169] that in the range
of pH 7-8 in the presence of $SO_4{}^{2-}$ ions, the complex
ions $(GeO_2(SO_4))^{2-}$ are adsorbed, and that in the
presence of $PO_4{}^{3-}$ ions, the ions $(HGeO_2(PO_4))^{2-}$
are formed.

In the presence of oxalate ions, germanium can be
separated from acid solutions on Amberlite IRA-400
in the form of complex oxalate ions.

A study of the adsorption of germanium on various
anion exchangers (four types were tested) showed
that it is possible to separate it to the extent of
90-95% from solutions with initial concentrations of
10-25 mg/l. [170] One of the ion exchangers can
adsorb germanium in amounts up to 14 mg/g of
resin. In solutions of pH 5-9, the exchange capacity
of the anion exchanger is approximately 100 times
greater than in the case of separation of germanium
from 0.7 N sulfuric acid   solutions.

It was found that by successively passing the washing solution through a series of columns packed with
the anion exchanger saturated with germanium, the
latter could be concentrated to 5-7 g/l.

The adsorption of germanium by cation-exchange
resins was studied.[171] Adsorption under static
conditions, carried out from 5% sulfuric acid
solutions containing 50 mg/l germanium dioxide,
showed that the cation exchanger ROAS, containing
a carboxyl and an OH-phenol group, adsorbs up to
1.1 mg/g of dry resin; KB-4P adsorbs only 0.2
mg/g of resin. Thus, despite the statements of
certain investigators,[168, 169] it is possible to
select cation exchangers capable of adsorbing germanium from acid solutions.

The adsorption of germanium from hydrochloric
acid solutions did not yield any appreciably better results, but the adsorption was considerably increased
by adding hydroxylamine hydrochloride to the initial
solution (1 g/100 ml of solution). Thus, the cation

exchanger KU-21 adsorbs 4.9 mg/g of dry resin, and KU-IG adsorbs 3.3 mg/g under the same conditions. The other cation exchangers studied did not adsorb germanium.

Thirty samples of various resins were prepared and tested.[171] The adsorption was carried out from 3-5% sulfuric acid solutions. The capacity of the majority of the resins was found to be fully satisfactory; thus, it was 8.7 mg/g of dry resin for samples of 118-Ge resin, 8.1 mg/g of resin for 122-Ge, and 3.5 mg/g for 105-Ge. The latter displayed a good selectivity in the adsorption of germanium from acid solutions in the presence of As^{3+}, As^{5+}, and Zn^{2+}.

A study of the desorption of germanium by acid and alkaline solutions showed that a 5% NaOH solution is best suited for this purpose. The anion is also simultaneously regenerated.

As is evident from the above material on germanium complex compounds, the latter are characterized by an abundance of forms.

10. ORGANOGERMANIUM COMPOUNDS

Organogermanium compounds are also quite diverse. In this respect, germanium resembles silicon.

Organogermanium compounds can be classified as follows: [2]

(a) Alkyl compounds of germanium hydrides of the type R_4Ge, $R_3Ge-GeR_3$, etc.;

(b) Compounds with halogenated germanium hydrides of the type R_4GeX_{4-n} (where R is an organic base and X is a halogen);

(c) Oxidized compounds of the type $(R_3Ge)_2O$;

(d) Compounds of the type $R_2Ge(OH)_2$;

(e) Esters of germanic acid $Ge(OR)_4$;

(f) Nitrogen compounds of germanium containing organic bases.

Metal-containing styrenes may undergo an extensive polymerization to form substances with a relatively high melting point.

The compound n - $(C_2H_2)_3$Ge- ⬡ -CH - CH_2 was synthesized in 35% yield; it has a melting point of 85°C and a density of 1.0740 g/cm^3. [179]

It was shown that HGeCl$_3$ adds readily to practically any unsaturated hydrocarbons without requiring activation or catalysts: [180]

$$Cl_3GeH + C=C \longrightarrow Cl_3GeC-CH.$$

HGeCl$_3$ is a more reactive compound than HSiCl$_3$.

By reacting perfluorovinylmagnesium iodide in an ether or tetrahydrofuran solution with halides or complex salts of germanium, it is possible to prepare tetraperfluorovinylgermanium, which has the formula $(CF_2=CF_2)_4$Ge. [181] Its boiling point is 123-124°C, refractive index 1.3662, and density

$1.7719 \ g/cm^3$. It is decomposed with difficulty by alkalis, and only on heating.

Results of measurements of the dipole moments of certain organogermanium compounds are given in Table 36. [182]

Tetramethoxygermane was obtained by the reaction $GeCl_4 + 4NaOCH_3 \longrightarrow Ge(OCH_3)_4 + 4NaCl.$ [183] Its boiling point is $145.5^{\circ}C$, and its density, $1.34 \ g/cm^3$. At room temperature, it is a colorless and mobile liquid.

Ethers of the type $Ge(OR)_4$ were obtained, where R is a methyl, ethyl, propyl, or butyl group. [184] The vapor pressures of these ethers obey the equation

$$\log P \ (mm \ Hg) = a - \frac{b}{T} \ ,$$

the coefficients of which are given in Table 37.

Germanium tetrachloride forms the compound $Ge(NC_6H_5)_2 \cdot 2HCl$ with aniline. [4] Ethylamine reacts with germanium tetrachloride to form $Ge(NC_2H_5)_2$. Tertiary amines reacting with germanium tetraiodide form aminates with five amine molecules. Other nitrogen compounds of germanium containing organic bases are also known. [4]

11. ELECTROCHEMICAL PROPERTIES OF GERMANIUM

The electrochemistry of germanium has been discussed fully in the monograph of E. A. Efimov and I. G. Erusalimchik. [204]

Germanium is close to hydrogen in the electromotive series. It displaces silver from solutions of its salts, but does not displace mercury and tin from chloride and nitrate solutions. [185]

The potential of the system Ge/Ge^{4+} in an acid medium is 0.13-0.15 V [185, 186] and in an alkaline medium, 1.0 V. According to an approximate estimate, the potential of the system Ge^{4+}/Ge^{2+} is 0.3 V, [185] and that of the system Ge/Ge^{2+}, 0.0 V relative to the standard hydrogen electrode. [1, 185]

Table 36, Characteristics of Certain Organogermanium Compounds.

Compound	Total Polarization P_{tot}	Molecular Refraction R_D	Atomic Polarization, P_{at}	Dipole Moment $\mu \times 10^{18}$
$(CH_3)GeCl_3$	183,2	31,7	8	2,63
$(CH_3)_2GeCl_2$	239,3	31,5	8	3,11
$(C_2H_5)GeCl_3$	214,8	35,6	8	2,87
$(C_2H_5)_2GeCl_2$	258,2	40,7	8	3,19
$(CH_3)_3GeCH \cdot Cl \cdot CH_3$	164,1	42,1	8	2,34
$Cl_3GeCH_2CH_2Cl$	165,7	41,2	8	2,41

In 2 N sulfuric acid, the hydrogen overvoltage of a copper electrode coated with germanium is 0.32 V, and on a solid germanium electrode the overvoltage is 0.25 V. [1]

In anodic polarization in solutions of acids and alkalis, germanium oxidizes to the tetravalent state and goes into solution in the form of complex ions. At high current densities, the oxidation products cannot dissolve, and therefore cover the surface of the electrode. Hydrogen is evolved in the presence of cathodic polarization on germanium.

In the electrolysis of aqueous solutions of germanium salts, germanium deposits at the cathode. However, as soon as a thin film of germanium covers the electrode, hydrogen begins to be evolved, since this process proceeds with a lower overvoltage than the deposition of germanium. For this reason, a germanium admixture present in the electrode-position of zinc, for example, is undesirable, and the permissible concentrations should not exceed 0.01 mg/l.

Table 37, Coefficient of the Equation Describing The Vapor Pressures of Germanium Esters.

Ester	a	b		Ester	a	b
Methyl	8,28	2300		Butyl	8,58	3260
Ethyl	8,33	2500		Isobutyl . . .	8,79	3130
Propyl	8,47	2870		Parabutyl . .	8,88	3130
Isopropyl . . .	8,76	2865		Metabutyl . .	8,41	2810

However, in the electrodeposition of alloys of germanium with other metals, the overvoltage is sufficiently low, and germanium codeposits with copper,
silver, nickel, and cobalt from solutions of
complex-forming agents. Thus, in the presence of
a fourfold excess of copper or a 1.5-fold excess of
nickel, germanium can be deposited quantitatively.
Good germanium coatings can be obtained by
electrolysis of nonaqueous solutions of germanium
tetrachloride, for example, in ethylene glycol or
propylene glycol. [186]

It was found that when n-type germanium dissolves, a saturation current is observed, whereas
in the case of p-type germanium this phenomenon is
absent.

At a current intensity considerably below the saturation current of n-germanium, a linear dependence
of the potential on the log of the anodic current
density was observed in both cases. It was found
that positive charge carriers, i.e., holes, are

necessary for the primary electrochemical reaction on the germanium anode. [187]

Alkaline solutions are widely used for the electro-chemical etching of germanium in the production of semiconductor devices. Experiments have shown that 10 or more monolayers of oxygen can be adsorbed on the surface of germanium. For this reason, it is probable that in the course of anodic dissolution, an oxide layer which begins to be cathodically reduced at $\varphi = 0.75$ V is formed on the germanium surface. [188]

Fast and slow polarization measurements were used to show that the overvoltage of hydrogen evolution on a p-type germanium cathode at potentials more negative than -0.6 V (zero charge potential of germanium) decreases somewhat when the electrode is hydrogenated. [189] This phenomenon is probably related to an inflection of the energy bands on the surface of the semiconductor as a result of the adsorption and penetration of hydrogen atoms into the crystal lattice. At current densities of 10^{-1}

A/cm^2, a sharp anomalous rise in the potential of
the p- and n-type germanium cathode is observed.
This influence is not observed on a degenerate semiconductor, so that it can be explained by the ohmic
drop of the potential in the depleted layer on the
surface of germanium and in the bulk of the semiconductor.

The electrochemical behavior of germanium has
been studied without external polarization and also
during cathodic and anodic polarization in 1 N acid,
neutral, and alkaline solutions (HCl, KCl, KOH).[190]
The values obtained for the steady-state potentials
make it possible to assert that there is virtually no
spontaneous dissolution of germanium in these
electrolytes. The only reaction of the anodic process is the ionization of hydrogen, which replaces
the anodic process of germanium dissolution. At
high current densities, a layer of oxides of white
(GeO_2) and orange color (GeO) is formed on the
surface of the germanium anode, i.e., the passivation
of the electrode takes place.

In aqueous solutions, the surface of germanium is usually covered with an oxide film. This was demonstrated by experiments on the anodic dissolution of germanium. A study of the nature of the variation in the electrode potential of the germanium anode with time at constant current density showed that in a dilute acid medium, not more than one electron per atom of germanium is required during the formation of the surface oxide or hydroxide layer. [191]

During the deposition of germanium not only from aqueous solutions but also melts, after the germanium film has appeared on the cathode, hydrogen begins to be evolved.

The deposition of germanium from alkaline solutions on a copper cathode proceeds very slowly until the copper is completely covered with a layer of germanium, and only then is hydrogen evolved. [1]

An insignificant deposition of germanium takes place at the mercury cathode in 0.1-8.0 N solutions of sulfuric acid at a current density of 0.1 A/cm^2 at room temperature. [1]

A number of organic solvents of germanium tetrachloride have been tested to determine whether this
metal can be deposited electrolytically. Ethylene
glycol and propylene glycol were found to be the
best solvents. Good, lustrous, high-purity germanium films are obtained at electrolysis temperatures of 50-60°C, current densities of 0.11-0.30
A/cm^2, and a germanium tetrachloride content in the
solution of about 3-7 vol. %. Under optimum conditions (7% solution of GeCl$_4$; T = 59°C; D = 0.4
A/cm^2), the deposition rate of germanium is 0.008
mm/hr. The coating is still lustrous at a thickness
of 0.127 mm. The process proceeds best in a
propylene glycol solution. The anode is made of
graphite.[192]

Similar results were obtained with the electro-
deposition of germanium from solutions of its
tetraiodide in glycerin, ethylene glycol, and other
organic solvents.[1]

The electrochemical cell Hg(Na) $|$ GeO$_2$, NaOH/Pt
yields GeH$_4$, Ge and H$_2$ as the cathodic products.
Such a cell can be used as a source of monogermane.[194]

The electroplating of various metals on germanium
has been carried out. The oxide films and residues
of the products of etching of germanium can be removed by cathodic reduction. This reduction in the
plating solutions is possible when the potential at
which the metal begins to deposit is more negative
than the potential necessary for the reduction of the
surface layer. Cyanide solutions are the most suitable for deposition on germanium.[195] The following metals have been successfully deposited on germanium: chromium, cobalt, nickel, rhodium and
platinum (from sulfate and chloride solutions), copper,
zinc, silver, gold, indium, cadmium (from cyanide
solutions), tin, antimony, tellurium, lead and bismuth (from haloborate and halide solutions). All the
electrolytically deposited metals with the exception

of antimony give a rectifying contact with n-type
germanium and an ohmic contact with p-type germanium.

The possibility of obtaining protective coatings
from tin-germanium and antimony-germanium
alloys in an alkali sulfide electrolyte has been demonstrated. [196] These coatings possess good anti-
corrosive properties. The coatings were deposited
on copper foil, and a graphite anode was used. In
order to obtain tin-germanium coatings, the starting
materials used were $SnCl_2 \cdot 5H_2O$ and germanium
dioxide, which were dissolved in a solution containing 90 g/l sodium hydroxide. The cathodic current density was 1.5 A/dm^2 at 65°C. The content
of germanium in the electrolyte was 4.5 g/l, and
that of tin, 45 g/l. The alloys obtained contained
from 10.0 to 61.6% germanium. The current efficiency did not exceed 17%. As the temperature
rose, the current efficiency increased. The thickness of the coatings reached 8 mμ. The antimony-

germanium alloy was deposited from a solution containing 180 g/l sodium hydroxide, 100 g/l sodium sulfide, 10 g/l antimony, and up to 10 g/l germanium. The optimum current density was 1.0 A/dm^2 at 40-60°C. Coatings of good quality which polished readily and contained up to 11.5% germanium were obtained at the cathode. The current efficiency was 65%.

Electrodeposition was used to prepare a copper-germanium alloy corresponding to the composition Cu_3Ge. The electrolysis was carried out in pyrophosphoric acid solutions. [185]

Certain alloys of germanium were obtained by electrolyzing a mixture of molten salts in a graphite crucible. Electrolytes of the composition $2GeO_2 \cdot Na_2O + 4NaF$ and $4SiO_2 \cdot Li_2O + GeO_2$ were used for this purpose. The primary cathodic product is the alkali metal, which reduces germanium dioxide to the metal.

Alloys of germanium with nickel obtained by electrolyzing the melt m · $(2GeO_2 · Na_2O) + NiO + 4NaF$ at 900-1000°C[185] were found to be a mixture of the intermetallic compounds NiGe, Ni_2Ge and a solid solution of germanium in nickel containing 20-25% Ge.

Alloys of germanium with iron were obtained in similar fashion. They consisted of a mixture of the compounds $FeGe_2$, Fe_2Ge, and solid solutions of germanium in iron containing 7.7-11.2% Ge. [185]

Compounds of germanium with manganese, chromium, molybdenum, and tungsten were obtained from melts. [186]

In order to obtain metallic germanium by electro-deposition, its dioxide is dissolved in a sodium tetraborate melt in the proportion of 1:1. The deposition is carried out in a graphite crucible with a graphite anode at 1000°C and a current density of 28 A/dm^2. [1] The current efficiency is approximately 58%, and the purity of the germanium

obtained exceeds 99.1%. A continuous process may
be carried out.

Pure germanium is also deposited from borate
melts.[193]

12. ANALYTICAL CHEMISTRY OF GERMANIUM

The analytical chemistry of germanium has been
treated in comprehensive review articles.[100, 197]

Depending upon the pH of the solution, germanium
is present either in a cationic or anionic form.
Thus, at pH below 4, germanium may be present in
either form.[197] Anionic forms of germanium
which appear at pH below 1 are anions of acid
complexes.

Tetravalent germanium is included in the analytical
group of hydrogen sulfide and belongs to the subgroup of acid sulfides together with arsenic, antimony,
manganese, molybdenum, etc. In contrast to arsenic
and tin, germanium disulfide is formed only in
strongly acidic solutions. It is hydrolyzed by water,

and therefore, a quantitative precipitation of germanium requires, in addition to a high acidity, the
presence of an excess of hydrogen sulfide during
the precipitation, filtration and washing of the
precipitate. Like tin, germanium is not precipitated
by hydrogen sulfide from solutions containing hydrofluoric and oxalic acids. Like silicon, arsenic, and
phosphorus, germanium readily forms complex
heteropoly acids with molybdenum and tungsten.
Like boron, germanium forms complex acids with
polyhydric alcohols and hydroxycarboxylic acids,
and also gives color reactions with hydroxyanthra-
quinones in concentrated sulfuric acid.

In its behavior toward tannin, germanium falls
into the same category with tin, niobium, tantalum and
titanium. However, in contrast to tin, titanium is
precipitated by tannin from less acidic media.

In its behavior toward organic compounds containing an orthohydroxyquinone grouping, germanium
is similar to elements of group IV of the periodic

system (Sn, Si, Zr, Hf), and also to certain elements of groups V and VI (Sb^{3+}, Nb, Ta, Mo, W).

The volatility of germanium tetrachloride facilitates its separation from associated elements.

In the concentration of germanium and its separation from other elements, use is also made of precipitation methods employing organic or inorganic precipitants, extraction, and ion exchange.

Qualitative Analysis

Distillation Process. Germanium tetrachloride is an important compound not only in analytical chemistry but also in the technology of germanium. Distilled as the tetrachloride, germanium is determined by a gravimetric or any other method. The greatest difficulties are encountered in its separation from arsenic. For this reason, the process is conducted in the presence of an oxidant in order to convert the volatile arsenic trichloride into the involatile arsenic pentachloride. Gaseous chlorine is the best oxidant. The method permits the detection of 0.5 mg of germanium dioxide in 100 g of arsenic trioxide. [100]

Precipitation Processes. Germanium is sometimes precipitated as the disulfide from a strongly acidic solution. The interfering arsenic is first removed as the sulfide from a dilute hydrochloric acid solution. The separation may be carried out by reducing the arsenic to the elemental state with sodium hypophosphite. At the same time, tetravalent germanium is reduced to the divalent state.

Potassium ferrocyanide is sometimes used to precipitate germanium from solution. A white precipitate of $(GeO_2)_2 \cdot Fe(CN)_6 \cdot 2H_2O$ is thus formed.

Germanium is virtually completely precipitated by tannin or tannides. Under certain precipitation conditions, germanium can be freed from many associated elements.

Hydrogen selenide in an aqueous solution of formaldehyde ties up germanium in the form of a yellow precipitate. The sensitivity of the determination is $2 \times 10^{-5}\%$.

Organic Reagents. The most sensitive reaction is that with phenylfluorone (9-phenyl-2,3,7-trihydroxy-6-fluorone). Filter paper is impregnated with a 0.05% solution of phenylfluorone in alcohol. The tested solution is adjusted to pH 1 with hydrochloric acid, a drop of this solution is placed on prepared filter paper, and the latter is then treated with concentrated nitric acid. The intensity of the pink coloration indicates the presence of germanium in the sample. Strong oxidants such as chromates, permanganates, or tetravalent cesium interfere with the determination. This method is also used for the quantitative determination of germanium.[198]

Germanium interacts with aromatic organic reagents having two hydroxyl groups in the ortho position or one group in the para position.[100] These reagents include alizarin and its derivatives, hydroxyazobenzene, etc.

Polyhydroxy alcohols such as glycerol and mannitol form complex acids with metagermanic acid. Complex acids are more dissociated, and for this reason the presence of germanium in the solution causes a decrease in the pH of the medium which is detected.

Molybdic Acid. Germanates react with molybdic acid to form molybdogermanic acid $H_8Ge(Mo_2O_7)_6$. In the presence of benzidine, this acid produces a deep coloration. It is first necessary to separate the interfering ions Sn^{2+}, Fe^{2+}, and As^{3+}. Arsenates, phosphates and silicates also interfere.[100]

Quantitative Analysis

Gravimetric Methods. The gravimetric form is usually germanium dioxide. Germanium compounds are converted into the dioxide by various methods. A common method is the precipitation of germanium as the sulfide. The germanium disulfide precipitate is oxidized either by roasting in air or by hydrogen peroxide in a medium of ammonia.

Germanium is quantitatively precipitated by a 5% solution of tannin. A white precipitate is thus formed which after calcining yields germanium dioxide. Chlorides interfere with the precipitation.

Magnesium orthogermanate Mg_2GeO_4 is precipitated from aqueous solutions containing tetravalent germanium by a mixture of magnesium and ammonium sulfate in a concentrated ammonia solution.

The precipitation of germanium in the form of salts of molybdogermanic or tungstogermanic acid by such organic bases as pyridine, cinchonine, and quinoline permits a gravimetric determination.

Like boron, germanium is determined in the form of barium germanium tartrate. [197] A tartrate of the composition $Ba_2GeC_8H_8O_{14} \cdot 2H_2O$ is formed. A complete precipitation of germanium is achieved only when acetone is added to the solution. Trivalent arsenic does not interfere.

Germanium can be determined in the form of phenylarsonate. Phenylarsonic and p-dimethylaminoazophenylarsonic acid are suitable for the quantitative determination of germanium. Precipitation by the first reagent is carried out from an acetic acid solution, and by the second reagent, from a 2.5-4.0 N solution of hydrochloric acid. The gravimetric forms can be both germanium arsonates and germanium dioxide, which is formed by calcining the arsonates. [197]

Among the gravimetric methods, the best ones are those involving the use of sulfide, tannin, orthohydroxyquinoline and dibromoorthohydroxyquinoline.

Volumetric Methods. Tetravalent germanium forms a complex compound with mannitol that is titrated with alkali. Germanium must first be separated as the sulfide. Treatment of this complex compound with a mixture of potassium iodate and iodide in the presence of strong electrolytes permits titration with sodium thiosulfate.

Another method involves the precipitation of the salt of molybdogermanic acid and any organic base, for example, pyridine, quinoline, etc. The precipitate is dissolved in a mixture of hydrochloric acid and ethyl alcohol, treated with a large amount of a bromide-bromate solution, and then with potassium iodide. Free iodine is titrated with sodium thiosulfate. [100]

Compounds of divalent germanium are stronger reductants than the analogous compounds of tin. For this reason, germanium can be determined with sufficient accuracy by the iodometric method, following a preliminary reduction with sodium hypophosphite to the divalent state. When reduced in a hydrochloric acid solution, germanium separates completely from arsenic. [199]

The alkalimetric determination is based on the use of polyhydric alcohols. When a polyhydric alcohol (or monosaccharide) is added to a neutral solution of germanium dioxide, the pH of the solution drops markedly because of the formation of a complex germanic acid. The titration is carried out with an alkali. If the original solution being analyzed gives an acid reaction, it is neutralized by the solution of alkali to pH 6-7, the polyhydric alcohol is added, and the complex acid of germanium is titrated in the presence of an indicator with a color change at pH 6-8. [197]

The precipitation of complex molybdenum-germanium salts with pyridine or quinoline also permits a volumetric determination of germanium. After washing, the precipitate of germanomolybdate is dissolved in 0.1 N sodium hydroxide, whose excess is back-titrated with hydrochloric acid. [197]

The separation of germanomolybdates of orthohy-droxyquinoline and dibromoorthohydroxyquinoline also permits a bromometric determination in the first case and a vanadometric determination in the second. [197]

The best methods for the volumetric determination
of germanium are alkalimetric ones involving the use
of fructose or inverted sucrose. Methods based on
the precipitation of germanomolybdates of orthohydroxyquinoline and dibromoorthohydroxyquinoline
are suited for the determination of small amounts
of germanium.

Photometric Methods. The intensity of the yellow
color of solutions containing a complex germanomolybdic acid obeys the Beer-Lambert law up to a
germanium concentration of 40 mg/l. The method
requires a preliminary treatment of the sample.[100]

Oxidized hematoxylin forms purple complex compounds with germanium. Other elements forming
heteropoly acids do not interfere. The method is
suited for the determination of germanium in concentrations of 8×10^{-6} to $1.6 \times 10^{-4}\%$.

One of the most common methods of photometric
determination of germanium is an analysis involving the use of phenylfluorone.[197] The reaction is

analogous to the qualitative reaction for germanium
on filter paper described above. In addition to
germanium, many elements of groups IV, V and VI -
Ti, Zr, Hf, Sn^{4+}, Sb^{3+}, Nb, Ta, Mo, W - react with
phenylfluorone. Germanium and antimony can
react with phenylfluorone at a higher acidity of the
solution than other elements. Phosphorus, arsenic
and silicon do not interfere with the phenylfluorone
determination of germanium.

In acid solutions, germanium and phenylfluorone
form an insoluble complex which, when the germanium content is low, remains in the colloidal
state, particularly after stabilization with a protective colloid. In a hydrochloric acid solution, the
protective colloid is gelatin, and in a sulfuric acid
solution, gum arabic. Hydrochloric acid solutions
of germanium phenylfluoronate stabilized with
gelatin obey the Beer-Lambert law in the range of
germanium concentrations of 0.01 to 5 mg/l. The
light absorption peak is located at 505-510 mμ. The

best protective colloid for germanium phenylfluoronate is polyvinyl alcohol.

Germanium is determined with phenylfluorone in a
0.5-1.0 N solution of hydrochloric acid. Germanium
phenylfluoronate does not dissolve in common organic
solvents, but is filtered off. This is used to increase the
sensitivity of the reaction.

In addition to phenylfluorone, other derivatives of
trihydroxyfluorone are used for the analysis of
germanium. The composition of the complex compound formed by germanium with phenyfluorone and
with other trihydroxyfluorones corresponds to the
ratio Ge : R = 1:2. In the trihydroxyfluorone
molecule, germanium replaces one hydrogen atom.
Other complex-forming agents are also used for the
photometric determination of germanium, for example, orthodiphenols, hematein (with an orthohydroxyquinone group), hydroxyflavones, hydroxy-
anthraquinones, derivatives of tripolone, dihydroxy-
chromenols, etc. [197,200]

Fluorometric Methods. Reagents giving fluorescent reactions with germanium are few, for example, hydroxyflavone-morin, benzoin, resacetophenone, and other aromatic compounds containing a hydroxy group in the ortho position.[197] These reactions are less sensitive than the above-described reactions used in the photometric determination.

Polarography of Germanium. The reduction of tetravalent germanium in alkaline and neutral buffer solutions is irreversible. The second polarographic wave observed in the course of this process is due to the reduction of hydrogen.[201] The half-wave potential of the reduction of tetravalent germanium to the metal on a mercury electrode in an ammonium chloride medium is 1.4 V.[202]

Divalent germanium in a hydrochloric acid solution is easily reduced to the metal on a dropping mercury electrode, giving rise to a marked diffusion current. The half-wave potential of the system Ge^{2+}/Ge in 6 N hydrochloric acid at a germanium concentration of

1×10^{-4} mole/l is equal to 0.45-0.50 V.[197] As
the concentration of hydrochloric acid decreases,
the potential shifts toward the positive side.

A polarographic method of determining germanium
in 6 N hydrochloric acid after the reduction of Ge^{4+}
to Ge^{2+} by phosphorous acid or sodium or potassium
hypophosphite was developed. Arsenic, antimony,
tin, copper, lead, and the chloride ion interfere with
the analysis. The chloride ion is bound up in the
complex anion $CdCl_2^{2-}$.[197] Prior to the determination, germanium is separated from the interfering
elements by distillation of the tetrachloride or by
extraction of the tetrachloride with carbon tetrachloride.

Spectral Analysis. The lines 2709.6, 2651.15,
2651.60, and 3039.08 Å are usually employed for
the determination of germanium.[100] The internal
standards used are copper (2768 Å line), bismuth
(2627.93 and 1993.34 Å) and platinum (2659.44 and
3064.71 Å). Sometimes it is necessary to enrich

the sample first, or to separate the germanium from
the interfering elements. The spectral method is
characterized by its simplicity and is suitable for
mass analyses of products of the same type.

Table 38 shows data on the sensitivity of the various
methods of determination of germanium.[197]

The determination of germanium in various rocks
and ores is complicated by its low concentration in
the samples. A still more difficult task in analytical
chemistry is the determination of impurities in semiconducting germanium. At the present time, impurities in germanium can be determined in concentrations of 10^{-5}-10^{-6}%. Radioactivation analysis as
well as color, fluorescent, and catalytic reactions
are used. It would be desirable to have methods
which would permit the determination of impurities
in amounts of 10^{-8}-10^{-9}%.[197]

Table 38, Sensitivity of Various Methods of Determination of Germanium.

Method	Sensitivity	Error, %
Gravimetric (determination of GeO_2)	Above 0.01 g In Sample	—
Volumetric (alkalimetric determination of Germanium in Industrial Concentrates)	Above 1.0%	—
Photometric		
with Germanomolybdic Blue	$1 \cdot 10^{-4}$ %	
with Phenylfluorone	$5 \cdot 10^{-5}$ %	±10
Polarographic	$1 \cdot 10^{-3}$ %	—
Spectral		
In Coal Ash	$1 \cdot 10^{-3}$ %	±12
In Oxidized Iron Ores and Coals	$1 \cdot 10^{-4}$ %	±6%
In Silicate Rocks	$5 \cdot 10^{-5}$ %	±15

REFERENCES

1. Gmelins Handbuch der anorganischen Chemie. System Nummer 45. Germanium. Erganzungsband, 1958.

2. E. Gastinger, Fortschritte der chemischen Forschung, 3, 603-656 (1955).

3. Kh. Navotnyi, Usp. Khim., 27, 8, 996-1009 (1958).

4. O. Johnson, Usp. Khim., 25, 1, 105-132 (1956).

5. A.N. Zelikman, G.V. Samsonov and O.E. Krein, Metallurgy of Rare Metals. Moscow, Metallurgizdat, 1954.

6. B.V. Nekrasov, Textbook of General Chemistry. Moscow, Goskhimizdat, 1954.

7. F.D. Rossini, D.D. Wagman, W.H. Evans, S. Levine and E. Jaffe, Selected Values of Chemical Thermodynamic Properties. Vol. 1 and 2. U.S. Government Printing Office, Washington, 1952.

8. H. Krebs, Angew. Chem., 11, 293-296 (1953).

9. P. Flubacher, A. L. Leadbetter and J. A. Morrison, Philos. Mag., 4, 39, 273-294 (1956).

10. A. W. Searcy, J. Amer. Chem. Soc., 74, 19, 4789-4791 (1952).

11. O. Kubaschewski and E. L. Evans, Metallurgical Thermochemistry. 2nd ed. New York, J. Wiley & Sons, 1956.

12. An. N. Nesmeyanov, Vapor Pressure of the Chemical Elements. Moscow, 1961.

13. R. E. Honig, J. Chem. Phys., 22, 9, 1610 (1954).

14. R. D. Freeman and A. W. Searcy, J. Chem. Phys., 23, 88 (1955).

15. V. D. Ignatkov and V. E. Kosenko, Fiz. Tverd. Tela, 3, 1, 89-93 (1961).

16. R. B. Bernstein and D. Cubiciotti, J. Amer. Chem. Soc., 73, 4112-4114 (1951).

17. J.T. Law and P.S. Meigs, J. Electrochem. Soc.,
    104, 3, 154-159 (1957).

18. J.R. Ligenza, J. Phys. Chem., 64, 8, 1017-
    1022 (1960).

19. V.G. Tronev and M.E. Chibireva, Zh. Neorg.
    Khim., 1, 10, 2278-2282 (1956).

20. E. Gastinger, Naturwissenschaften, 42, 4, 95
    (1955).

21. O. Roesner, Z. Metallkunde, 48, 3, 137-142
    (1957).

22. R. Kh. Burshtein, L.A. Larina and G.F.
    Voronina, Dokl Akad. Nauk SSSR, 133, 1, 148-
    151 (196).

23. E.D. Devyatkova and I.A. Smirnov, Zh. Tekhn.
    Fiz., 27, 9, 1944-1949 (1957).

24. V.M. Glazov and D.A. Petrov, Izv. Akad. Nauk
    SSSR, OTN, 2, 15-19 (1958).

25. L. Graf, H. R. Lacour and K. Seiler, Probl. Sovr. Metallurg., 3, 15, 105-107 (1954).

26. R. P. Carreker, J. Metals, 8, 2, 110-113 (1956).

27. E. M. Savitskii and V. F. Terekhova, Chemistry of Rare Elements. IONKh im. N. S. Kurnakov, No. 2, Akad, Nauk SSSR, Moscow, 1955, pp. 156-160.

28. S. E. Bradshaw, J. Electrochem. Soc., 101, 6, 293-297 (1954).

29. V. B. Lazarev and P. P. Pugachevich, Dokl. Akad. Nauk SSSR, 134, 1, 132-133 (1960).

30. T. P. Kolesnikova, Izvest. Vyssh. Uch. Zav., Chern. Metallurg., 9, 14-17 (1960).

31. B. I. Boltaks, Diffusion In Semiconductors. Moscow, Fizmatgiz, 1961.

32. A. J. Rozenberg, J. Phys. Chem., 62, 9, 1112-1119 (1958).

33. J.D. Thomas, Acta metallurgica, 9, 4, 388-389 (1961).

34. H. Letow, L.M. Slifkin and B. Portnow, Phys. Rev., 93, 4, 892 (1954).

35. W. H. Watson, J. Appl. Phys., 32, 1, 120-121 (1961).

36. G.S. Supin, Zh. Prikl. Khim., 32, 3, 478-481 (1959).

37. K.J. Miller, J. Electrochem. Soc., 108, 3, 296-297 (1961).

38. M.C. Cretella and H.C. Gatos, J. Electrochem. Soc., 105, 9, 487-496 (1958).

39. W.W. Harvey and H.C. Gatos, J. Electrochem. Soc., 105, 11, 654-659 (1958).

40. W.W. Harvey and H.C. Gatos, J. Electrochem., Soc., 107, 2,65-72 (1960).

41. E.A. Efimov and I.G. Erusalimchik, Zh, Fiz. Khim., 34, 3, 543-547 (1961).

42. O.G. Deryagin, E.N. Paleolog and N.D. Tomashev, Zh. Fiz. Khim., 34, 9, 1952-1959 (1960).

43. E.N. Paleolog, A.Z. Fedotova and N.D. Tomashev, Dokl. Akad. Nauk SSSR, 129, 3, 623-626 (1959).

44. D.R. Turner, J. Electrochem. Soc., 107, 10, 810-816 (1960).

45. V.S. Sotnikov and A.S. Belanovskii, Zh. Fiz. Khim., 35, 3, 509-512 (1961).

46. I.M. Kuleshov and A.F. Naumova, Zh. Fiz. Khim., 32, 1, 62-66 (1958).

47. I.V. Tananaev, M. Ya. Shpirt and T.I. Sendul'skaya, Dokl. Akad. Nauk SSSR, 139, 4, 907-909 (1961).

48. T.I. Sendul'skaya and M. Ya. Shpirt, Dokl. Akad. Nauk SSSR, 134, 5, 1108-1110 (1960).

49. E. G. Svirchevskaya and E. I. Ponomareva, _Izv._
    Akad. Nauk Kaz. SSSR. Ser. Metallurg.,
    Obogashch. i Ogneup., No. 1, 3-14 (1960).

50. E. A. Boom, _Chemistry of Rare Elements._ No.
    1, IONKh Akad. Nauk SSSR, Moscow, 1954,
    pp. 121-130.

51. M. Hansen and K. P. Anderko, _Constitution of_
    Binary Alloys. Transl. from German. New York,
    McGraw-Hill Book Co., 1957.

52. W. Freundlich and M. Bishara, _Bull. Soc._
    Chim. France, 5, 709-712 (1959)

53. G. F. Voronin and A. M. Evseev, _Zh. Fiz._
    Khim., 33, 9, 2024-2029 (1959).

54. E. S. Makarov and V. N. Bykov, _Kristallo-_
    grafiya, 4, 183-185 (1959).

55. N. Z. de Roche, _Z. Metallkunde_, 48, 2, 59-60
    (1957).

56. E.M. Savitskii, V.V. Baron and M.A. Tylkina, Zh. Neorg. Khim., 3, 3 762-775 (1958).

57. K. Anderko, Z. Metallkunde, 49, 4, 165-172 (1958).

58. N.V. Ageev, Yu. M. Golutvin and V.P. Samsonov, Zh. Neorg. Khim., 6, 8, 1864-1872 (1959).

59. A. Epstein and J. Geib, J. Electrochem. Soc., 106, 11, 995 (1959).

60. B.V. Mitrenin, N.E. Troshin, K.P. Tsomaya, V.A. Vlasenko and Yu. D. Gubanov, Problems of the Metallurgy and Physics of Semiconductors, Akad. Nauk SSSR, Moscow, 1957, pp. 59-69.

61. P. Popper and S.N. Ruddlesden, Nature, 179, 4570, 1129 (1957).

62. I.G. Fakidov and N.P. Grazhdankina, Fizika Met. i Metallov., 6, 1, 67-73 (1958).

63. N. Kh. Abrikosov, A. M. Vasserman and L. V. Poretskaya, Dokl. Akad. Nauk SSSR, 123, 2 279-281 (1958).

64. Z. U. Borisova, R. L. Myuller and Chin Ch'engts'ai, Zh. Prikl. Khim., 4, 35, 774-777 (1962).

65. I. G. Fakidov and Yu. N. Tsiovkin, Fizika Met. i Metallov., 7, 5, 685-688 (1959).

66. A. A. Bugai, V. E. Kosenko and E. G. Miselyuk, Zh. Tekh. Fiz., 37, 1, 210-211 (1957).

67. S. Bhan and K. Schubert, Z. Metallkunde, 51, 6, 327-339 (1960).

68. W. Burkhardt and K. Schubert, Z. Metallkunde, 50, 4, 196-198 (1959).

69. J. H. Foley and G. V. Rayonr, Trans. Faraday Soc. 57, 1, 51-60 (1961).

70. P. Greenfield and G. V. Raynor, J. Institute of Metals, 80, 7, 375-384 (1952).

71. L.J. Hutter and H.H. Stadelmaier, Z. Metallkunde, 50, 4, 199-203 (1959).

72. E.E. Cherkashin, E.I. Gladyshevskii, P.I.
Kripyakevich and Yu. V. Kuz'ma, Zh. Neorg.
Khim., 3, 3, 650-653 (1958).

73. H. Pflister, Acta Cryst., 11, 221-224 (1958).

74. E.S. Candidus and D. Tuomi, J. Chem. Phys.,
23, 588 (1955).

75. M. Hoch and H.L. Johnston, J. Chem. Phys.,
22, 8, 1376-1377 (1954).

76. L.M. Dennis and R.E. Hulse, J. Amer. Chem.
Soc., 52, 3553 (1930).

77. D.A. Everest and H. Terry, J. Chem. Soc.,
10, 2282-2285 (1950).

78. W.L. Jolly and W.M. Latimer, J. Amer. Chem.
Soc., 74, 22, 5751-5752 (1952).

79. G.A. Bergman and E.I. Shmuk, Izv. AN SSSR,
OTN, Metallurgiya i Toplivo, 1, 60-66 (1962).

80. W. L. Jolly and W. M. Latimer, J. Amer.
    Chem. Soc., 74, 22, 5757-5758 (1952).

81. W. Bues and H. von Wartenberg, Z. anorg.
    allgem. Chemie, 266, 6, 281-288 (1951).

82. V. I. Davydov and N. P. Diev, Trudy Inst.
    Metallurg. UFAN SSSR, No. 4, 23-34 (1958).

83. M. Ryczek, Hutnik, 10, 409-413 (1959).

84. J. A. O'Connor, Chem. Engin., 59, 4, 158-
    160 (1952).

85. J. A. Gay, Chemical and Process Engin., 34, 6
    175-179 (1953).

86. E. Gastinger, Z. anorg. allgem. Chemie, 285,
    1-2, 103-112 (1956).

87. V. I. Davydov, Behavior of Termanium During
    Roasting of Sulfide Concentrates. Author's
    abstract of dissertation for the degree of Can-
    didate of Technical Sciences. Sverdlovsk,
    UFAN SSSR, 1958.

88. G.A. Bergman, Zh. Neorg. Khim., 3, 10, 2422-2424 (1958).

89. A.W. Laubengayer and D.S. Morton, J. Amer. Chem. Soc., 54, 6, 2303 2320 (1932).

90. A. Pflugmacher and J. Kellerman, Z. angew. Chemie, 68, 374 (1956).

91. G. Brauer and H. Renner, Z. anorg. allgem. Chemie, 278, 1/2, 108-112 (1955).

92. Manual of Inorganic Preparations, ed. by G. Brauer. Moscow, IL, 1956.

93. P.N. Kovalenko and L.B. Reznik, Izv. Vyssh. Ucheb. Zav. Khim. i Khim. Tekhn., 2, 193-198 (1961).

94. I.V. Tananaev and K.A. Avduevskaya, Zh. Neorg. Khim., 3, 9, 2165-2171 (1958).

95. I.V. Tananaev and K.A. Avduevskaya, Zh. Neorg. Khim., 3, 9, 2172-2177 (1958).

96. I.N. Tselik and N.F. Turkanov, Ukr. Khim.
    Zh., 28, 2, 179-185 (1962).

97. E.V. Britske, A.F. Kapustinskii, B.K.
    Veselovskii et al., Thermal Constants of
    Inorganic Compounds, Moscow-Leningrad,
    Akad. Nauk SSSR, 1949.

98. K.K. Kelly and A.U. Christenson, U.S. Bureau
    of Mines Rept. Invest. 5710, 1961, p.5.

99. S.A. Shchukarev and G.A. Semenov, Dokl.
    Akad. Nauk SSSR, 120, 5, 1059-1061 (1958).

100. H.H. Krause and O.H. Johnson, Anal. Chem.,
     25, 1, 134-138 (1953).

101. E. Shimazaki, N. Matsumoto and K. Niwa, Bull.
     Chem. Soc. Japan, 30, 969-971 (1957).

102. T. Yokokawa, M. Kaizumi, M. Shimoji and K.
     Niwa, J. Amer. Chem. Soc., 79, 13, 3365-
     3367 (1957).

103. L.M. Dennis, K.M. Tressler and F.E. Hance,
     J. Amer. Chem. Soc., 45, 9, 2033-2047 (1923).

104. O. Rösner, Probl. Sovr. Metallurg., 5, 90-101 (1955).

105. V.I. Davydov, B.V. Teplyakov and G.K. Romanov, Zh. Prikl. Khim., 35, 7, 1625-1629 (1962).

106. V.I. Davydov, A.M. Belikov, N.I. Ignat'eva and D.E. Verbovetskaya, Zh. Prikl. Khim., 11 (1962).

107. O.A. Esin and P.V. Gel'd, Physical Chemistry of Pyrometallurgical Processes, Pts. 1 and 2, Sverdlovsk, Metallurgizdat, 1950 and 1954.

108. H. Strunz, Naturwissenschaften, 47, 7, 154-155 (1960).

109. P.P. Budnikov and S.G. Tresvyatskii, Dokl. Akad, Nauk SSSR, 94, 5, 761-763 (1954).

110. S.G. Tresvyatskii, Dopov. Akad. Nauk Ukr. SSR, 3, 295-298 (1958).

111. E.R. Shaw, J.F. Corwin and J.W. Edwards, J. Amer. Chem. Soc., 80, 7, 1536-1539 (1958).

112. G. Krüger and E. Thilo, Z. phys. Chem., 209, 3-4, 190-205 (1958).

113. E.I. Speranskaya and I.B. Barskaya, Izv. Akad. Nauk SSSR, Otd. khim. nauk, 8, 1495-1496 (1959).

114. E.I. Speranskaya, Zh. Neorg. Khim., 5, 2, 421-432 (1960).

115. A. Ya. Zvorykin, F.M. Perel'man, I.A. Babievskaya and T.N. Fedotova, Zh. Neorg. Khim., 5, 8, 1717-1724 (1960).

116. V.F. Zhuralev, Dokl. Akad. Nauk SSSR, 59, 6, 1145-1147 (1948).

117. M.A. Men'kovskii, S.A. Gordon and V.F. Churbakov, Dokl. Akad. Nauk SSSR, 144, 2, 367-370 (1962).

118. G. Gelsdorf, H. Muller-Hesse, H.E. Schweite, Archiv Eisenhuttenwesen, 8, 513-519 (1958).

119. A. Pelugmacher, D. Schorning and R. Schwarz, Z. anorg. allgem. Chemie, 295, 1-2, 93-105 (1958).

120. I. V. Tananaev and K. A. Avduevskaya, Zh. Neorg. Khim., 5, 1, 63-67 (1960).

121. W. C. Johnson, L. S. Foster and C. A. Kraus, J. Amer. Chem. Soc., 57, 1828-1830 (1935).

122. E. Gastinger, Z. Naturforschung, 10b, 2, 115-116 (1955).

123. Handbook of Chemistry and Physics. Ed. C. D. Hodgmann. Cleveland, Ohio, 33rd Edition, 1951-1952.

124. H. Spandau and F. Klanberg, Z. anorg. allgem. Chemie, 295, 5-6, 291-299 (1958).

125. W. C. Johnson and A. C. Wheatley, Z. anorg. allgem. Chemie, 216, 274-278 (1934).

126. R. F. Barrow, P. G. Dodsworth, G. Drummond and E. A. Jeffries, Trans. Faraday Soc., 51, 11, 1480-1482 (1955).

127. H. Kenworthy and A.G. Starliper, Probl. Sovr. Metallurg., 1, 31, 88-94 (1957).

128. E. Shimazaki and T. Wada, Bull. Soc. Japan, 29, 294-296 (1956).

129. V.I. Davydov and N.P. Diev, Zh. Neorg. Khim., 2, 9, 2003-2006 (1957).

130. K. Sudo, Sci, Repts. Res. Inst. Tohoku Univ., A12, 1, 54-61 (1960).

131. G.N. Sosnovskii and M.A. Abdeev, Izv. Akad. Nauk Kaz. SSR. Ser. Metallurg., Obogashch. i Ogneup., No. 2, 11, 3-9 (1961).

132. K. Ono and K. Sudo, Bull. Res. Inst. Min. Dressing and Met. Tohoku Univ., 10, 181-188 (1954).

133. A.I. Okunev, M.D. Galimov and A.A. Vostryakov, Dokl. Akad. Nauk SSSR, 140, 6, 1384-1387 (1961).

134. M.D. Galimov and A.I. Okunev, Izv. Vyssh. Ucheb. Zav., Tsvetn. Metallurg., 3, 94-104 (1961).

135. N.P. Diev and V.I. Davydov, Izv. Vost. Filialov Akad. Nauk SSSR, 7, 60-66 (1957).

136. S.V. Ivanov and V.I. Davydov, Zh. Neorg. Khim., 3, 4, 1060-1061 (1958).

137. A.D. Pogorelyi and N.K. Morozova, Izv. Vyssh. Ucheb. Zav., Tsvetn. Metallurg., 4, 113-121 (1960).

138. E. Shimazaki and N. Matsumoto, Nippon Kagaku Zasshi., 77, 1089-1091 (1956).

139. V.I. Bibikova and I.I. Vasilevskaya, Tr. Gidredmeta, Vol. 1. Moscow, Metallurgizdat, 1959.

140. V.I. Davydov and N.P. Diev, Zh. Prikl. Khim., 32, 2, 441-442 (1959).

141. A.N. Baraboshkin, Trudy UPI im. S.M. Kirova, 81, 166-178 (1959).

142. Liu Chün-hua, A.S. Pashinkin and A.V. Novoselova, Zh. Neorg. Khim., 7, 5, 963-966 (1962).

143. N. Bartlett and K.C. Ju, Canad. J. Chem., 39, 80-86 (1961).

144. W. L. Jolly and W. M. Latimer, J. Amer. Chem. Soc., 74, 22, 5752-5754 (1952).

145. W. L. Jolly and W. M. Latimer, J. Amer. Chem. Soc., 74, 22, 5754-5757 (1952).

146. J.I. Carasso and I. Stelzer, J. Chem. Soc., 4, 1797-1803 (1960).

147. D.A. Kochkin, M. F. Shostakovskii and L. V. Musagova, Zh. Prikl. Khim., 32, 7, 1614-1616 (1959).

148. A.I. Mel'nikov, Zh. Neorg. Khim., 2, 2, 233-237 (1957).

149. V.I. Evdokomov, Zh. Neorg. Khim., 3, 5, 1232-1236 (1958).

150. N.N. Murach, V.V. Krapukhin, F.S. Kulikov, V.N. Chernyaev and L.G. Nekhamkin, Zh. Prikl. Khim., 34, 10, 2188-2194 (1961).

151. P. Almanashu and A. Barzanfalvi,
Nohézbegyipari Kutató int. Közl., 1, 3-4, 297-
301 (1959).

152. V.G. Tronev and V.G. Lebedev, Zh. Neorg.
Khim., 3, 10, 2272-2275 (1958).

153. C. Devin, C.R. Acad. Sci., 247, 25, 2372-
2375 (1958).

154. S. Sujishi and I.N. Keith, J. Amer. Chem. Soc.,
80, 16, 4138-4140 (1958).

155. D.T. Hurd, Chemistry of the Hydrides. New
York, J. Wiley & Sons, Inc., 1952.

156. E. Amberger, Angew. Chemie, 11, 56-57 (1959).

157. V.A. Leitsin, Tsvet. Met., 3, 44-49 (1959).

158. D.S. Konovalov and E.N. Migotina, Zh. Prikl.
Khim., 33, 9, 1995-2001 (1960).

159. A.H. Zeltmann and G.C. Fitzgibbon, J. Amer.
Chem. Soc., 76, 7, 2021-2022 (1954).

160. V.A. Ponomarenko, G. Ya. Vzenkova and Yu. P. Egorov, Dokl. Akad. Nauk SSSR, 122, 3, 405-408 (1958).

161. V.G. Lebedev and V.G. Tronev, Zh. Neorg. Khim., 5, 8, 1725-1729 (1960).

162. E. Ya. Rode and M.M. Ivanova, Zh. Neorg. Khim., 3, 10, 2332-2342 (1958).

163. F.M. Perel'man, A. Ya. Zvorykin and T.N. Yakubovskaya, Zh. Neorg. Khim., 3,6, 1374-1380 (1958).

164. Z.F. Shakhova, G.N. Tishchenko and R.K. Motorkina, Zh. Obshch. Khim., 27, 5, 1118-1124 (1957).

165. A.I. Kokorin and N.A. Polotebneva, Zh. Obshch. Khim., 24, 10, 1718-1721 (1954).

166. D.A. Everest and J.C. Harrison, J. Chem. Soc., 4, 1745-1752 (1960).

167. D.A. Everest and J.C. Harrison, J. Chem. Soc., 10, 3752-3758 (1960).

168. D.A. Everest and J.E. Salmon, J. Chem. Soc.,
     7, 2438 (1954).

169. D.A. Everest and J.E. Salmon, J. Chem. Soc.,
     5, 1444 (1955).

170. A.K. Sharova, I.G. Chufarova, M.V. Vittikh
     and F.T. Shostak, Izv. Sib. Otd. Akad. Nauk
     SSSR, 8, 36-42 (1959).

171. F.T. Shostak, M.V. Vittikh, A.K. Sharova and
     I.G. Chufarova, Izv. Sib. Otd. Akad. Nauk
     SSSR, 8, 69-74 (1960).

172. P.J. Antikainen, Suomen Kem., 31, 9, 291-293
     (1958).

173. P.J. Antikainen, Suomen Kem., 32, 10, 211-
     213 (1959).

174. P.J. Antikainen, Suomen Kem., 32, 10, 214-
     219 (1959).

175. P.J. Antikainen, Suomen Kem., 32, No. 9,
     179-182 (1959).

176. O. Vartapetian, <u>Ann. Chemie.</u> 2, No. 11-12, 916-964 (1957).

177. W. Menzer, <u>Angew. Chemie</u>, 70, 21, 656 (1958).

178. D. Seyferth and N. Kahlen, <u>J. Amer. Chem. Soc.</u>, 82, No. 5, 1080-1082 (1960).

179. A. D. Petrov, E. A. Chernyshev and T. L. Krasnova, <u>Dokl. Akad. Nauk SSSR</u>, 140, 4, 837-840 (1961).

180. N. G. Dzhurinskaya, V. F. Mironov and A. D. Petrov, <u>Dokl. Akad. Nauk SSSR</u>, 138, 5, 1107-1110 (1961).

181. R. N. Sterlin, S. S. Dubov, Li Wei-kang, L. P. Vakhomchik and I. L. Knunyants, <u>Zh. Vsesoyuz. Khim. Obshch. im. D. I. Mendeleeva,</u> 6, 1, 110-111 (1961).

182. G. N. Kartsev, Ya. K. Syrkin and V. F. Mironov, <u>Izv. Akad. Nauk SSSR, Otd. Khim. Nauk,</u> 5, 948-949 (1960).

183. R. Schwarz and K.G. Knauff, Z. anorg. allgem. Chemie, 275, 4-5, 193-197 (1954).

184. D.C. Bradley, L.J. Kay, J.D. Schwanwick and W. Wardlaw, J. Chem. Soc., No. 10, 3656-3659 (1958).

185. R. Sh. Nigmetova, Trudy Inst. Khim. Nauk Akad. Nauk Kaz. SSR, 6, 178-183 (1960).

186. Yu. V. Pleskov, Khim. Nauka i Prom., 3, 4, 443-448 (1958).

187. Yu. A. Vdovin, V.G. Levich and V.A. Myamlin, Dokl. Akad. Nauk SSSR, 126, 6, 1296-1299 (1959).

188. E.A. Efimov and I.G. Erusalimchik, Dokl. Akad. Nauk SSSR, 134, 6, 1387-1389 (1960).

189. E.A. Efimov and I.G. Erusalimchik, Zh. Fiz. Khim., 34, 12, 2804-2807 (1960).

190. I.V. Borovkov, Zh. Fiz. Khim., 34, 12, 2682-2686 (1960).

191. W.W. Harvey, S. Sheff and H.C. Gatos,
     J. Electrochem. Soc., 107, 6, 560-562 (1960).

192. G. Szekely, J. Electrochem. Soc., 98, 8, 318-
     324 (1951).

193. V.N. Maslov, Yu. V. Granovskii and V.D.
     Samygin, Zh. Prikl. Khim., 32, 11, 2571-
     2574 (1959).

194. M. Green and P.H. Robinson, J. Electrochem.
     Soc., 106, 3, 253-260 (1959).

195. D.R. Turner, J. Electrochem. Soc., 106, 9,
     786-790 (1959).

196. S.I. Sklyarenko, I.I. Larov and S.V. Yakobson,
     Izv. Vyssh. Ucheb. Zaved., Tsvet. Metallurg.,
     2, 129-134 (1962).

197. V.A. Nazarenko, Methods of Determination and
     Analysis of Rare Elements. Akad. Nauk SSSR,
     Moscow, 1961, pp. 400-456.

198. B.M. Lipshitz and G.K. Smirnova, Zavod.
     Labor., 3, 273-274 (1960).

199. B.N. Ivanov-Emin, Zavod. Labor., 2, 161-163 (1947).

200. L.I. Kononenko and N.S. Poluektov, Zh. Anal. Khim., No. 1, 61-68 (1960).

201. V.P. Gladyshev and T.G. Kiseleva, Trudy Inst. Khim. Nauk, Akad. Nauk Kaz. SSR, 6, 184-195 (1960).

202. R. Sh. Nigmetova and M.T. Kozlovskii, Trudy Inst. Khim. Nauk, 6, 144-151 (1960).

203. G. Brauer and H. Müller, Z. anorg. allgem. Chemie, 287, 71 (1956).

204. E.A. Efimov and I.G. Erusalimchik, Electro-chemistry of Germanium and Silicon (translated by A. Peiperl). Washington, Sigma Press, 1963.

205. Selected Constants Relative to Semiconductors. Pergamon Press, Oxford-London-Paris-New York-Los Angeles-Frankfurt, 1961, p. 6.

RADIOACTIVE ISOTOPES

OF GERMANIUM

by N. P. Rudenko and

L. V. Kovtun, Atomizdat, 1964

ANNOTATION

This brochure discusses the radiochemistry of germanium, the nuclear processes by which its radioisotopes are formed, the methods used for their separation from the irradiated material, and the methods of measurement. The use of germanium radioisotopes in various research areas is examined.

The brochure is addressed to readers having an elementary knowledge of nuclear physics and chemistry and interested in radiochemistry and in the applied aspects of radioisotopes. It will be useful also to specialists concerned with the chemistry and technology of germanium and its compounds and alloys.

CONTENTS

1. Introduction

Germanium is a chemical element of group IV of
the periodic table with atomic number 32 and atomic
weight 72.60. The existance and properties of germanium were predicted in 1871 by D.I. Mendeleev
on the basis of the periodic law which he discovered.
Fifteen years later, K. Winkler observed in the
mineral argyrodite a new element which he called
germanium in honor of his country.

The content of germanium in the earth's crust is
$7.0 \times 10^{-4}\%$. Germanium is one of the trace elements,
since its bulk is not present in the few existing germanium minerals (which do not form large aggregates)
but is found as an impurity in the sulfide ores of nonferrous metals. Such ores, containing from 0.0001
to 0.1% germanium, are the main source of its production. Germanium is found in coals and oil shales.
A second source for the production of germanium is
coal ash, wastes of the by-product coke industry, and
slimes resulting from gasification.

N. P. Rudenko and
L. V. Kovtun, Atomizdat

The infrequent occurrence of germanium in nature and the high cost of its production have been and remain the causes of the insufficient study of the chemical properties of germanium.

The observed valuable property of germanium as a semiconductor has brought about its widespread use in radio and electronic engineering.

Single-crystal germanium can be used for the dosimetry of radioactive radiations and as a transducer for the conversion of light energy into electrical energy. The most significant application of germanium is its use in infrared technology, since it is capable of transmitting infrared radiation.

The presence of germanium in human blood and milk indicates its important physiological role. However, all the studies made thus far do not permit any definite conclusions in this regard.

It follows from the above that the role of germanium in the physiology of living organisms can be studied

only with minimum amounts of germanium. The
development of an improved technology of recover-
ing germanium from the raw material, where its
content is always low, and a more detailed study of
the chemistry of germanium can be carried out by
using its radioactive isotopes with a greater degree
of success, and in some cases, only by means of
radioactive tracers.[2-4]

2. Isotopes of Germanium

One of the reasons for the infrequent use of radiogermanium are the relatively inconvenient radio-
metric characteristics of the only radioactive isotope
of germanium, Ge^{71}, available in the USSR. As can
be seen from the table of germanium isotopes (Table
1), certain other radioactive isotopes whose production does not involve any appreciable difficulties
are better tracers. Natural germanium is made up
of four stable isotopes, Ge^{70}, Ge^{72}, Ge^{73}, Ge^{74} and
a single radioactive isotope Ge^{76}, which has a very
long half-life. Radioactive germanium isotopes are

N. P. Rudenko and
L. V. Kovtun, Atomizdat

Table 1, Isotopes of Germanium

Isotope	Half-life	Reaction of isotope formation	Character of radiation	Radiation energy, MeV nuclear particles	γ rays
Ge^{65}	1,5 min	Zn^{64} (α, 3n) Ge^{65}	β+; γ	3,7	0,67; 1,72
Ge^{66}	150 min	As^{75} (d, α 7n)Ge^{66}; Zn^{64} (α, 2n) Ge^{66}	β+; γ		0,045(100%); 0,070 (20%); 0,114 (50%); 0,186;
Ge^{67}	21 min	As^{75} (d, α 6n) Ge^{67}; Zn^{64} (α, n) Ge^{67}	β+; γ	2,9	0,17; 0,68; 0,86; 1,47
Ge^{68}	280 days	As^{75} (d, α 5n) Ge^{68}; Zn^{66} (α, 2n) Ge^{68}	EC		no γ radiation
Ge^{69}	40,4 hr	Ge^{70} (n, 2n) Ge^{69}; Daughter $As71$; Ga^{69} (d, 2n) Ge^{69}; Zn^{66} (α, n) Ge^{69}	EC(67%); β+ (33%) γ	1,215 (88%); 0,610 (10%); 0,22 (2%)	0,090; 0,388; 0,576; 0,870; 1,12; 1,34; 1,61
Ge^{70}		Stab 20,55%			
Ge^{71}	11,4 day	Ge^{70} (n, γ) $Ge71$; Daughter $As71$; As^{75} (d, α 2n) $Ge71$; Ga^{71} (d, 2n) $Ge71$; Ge^{70} (d, p) $Ge71$	EC		no γ radiation
Ge^{72}		27,37% stable			
Ge^{73}		7,61% stable			

Table 1 (cont)

Isotope	Half-life	Reaction of isotope formation	Character of radiation	Radiation energy, MeV	
				nuclear particles	γ rays
Ge^{73m}	0,53 sec	Ge^{72} (n, γ) Ge^{73m} Daughter As^{73}	IT		0,0135; 0,0539
Ge^{74}		36,74% stable			
Ge^{75m}	48 sec	Ge^{74} (n, γ) Ge^{75m} Ge^{74} (d, p) Ge^{75m} U^{235} (n, f)	IT		0,139
Ge^{75}	82 min	Ge^{74} (n, γ) Ge^{75} Ge^{76} $(n, 2n)$ Ge^{75} As^{75} (n, p) Ge^{75} Se^{78} (n, α) Ge^{75} U^{235} (n, f)	β^-; γ	1,14 (85%); 0,613 (15%)	0,066 (2.2%); 0,199 (12%); 0,264 (100%); 0,427 (2.5%); 0,477 (2,3%); 0,628 (1,8%)
Ge^{76}	2×10^6 yr	7,67 %			
Ge^{77m}	54 sec	Ge^{76} (n, γ) Ge^{77m} Ge^{76} (d, p) Ge^{77m} U^{235} (n, f)	β^- (86%) IT (14%)	2,7	0,159 (100% with IT); 0,215 (100%)
Ge^{77}	11,3 hr	Ge^{76} (n, γ) Ge^{77} Ge^{76} (d, p) Ge^{77} U^{235} (n, f)	β^-; γ	2,196 (42%); 1,379 (35%); 0,71 (23%)	Complex spectrum
Ge^{78}	86 days	U^{235} (n, f)	β^-	0,9	
Ge^{79}	<1 days		β^-		

N. P. Rudenko and

                                              L. V. Kovtun

obtained artificially by means of various nuclear re-

actions. Isotopes with the highest atomic weight are

formed in low yield, like the fission products of

uranium, thorium and other heavy elements, under

the influence of neutrons. Many of them can be used

as tagged atoms. The separation of these isotopes

has been described in the literature for Ge^{71} only.

Thus far, this is the only germanium isotope which

has found practical applications.

To determine the quantity of most germanium

radioisotopes, the usual methods of measuring β

and γ activity can be used. The choice of the method

of measuring the activity of each isotope should be

based on its half-life and on the decay scheme of the

isotope, i. e. , on the nature and energy of the radia-

tion characterizing this isotope. For example, the

1.5-minute Ge^{65} decays by emitting high-energy

positrons and γ rays. Its activity can be evaluated

by means of a proportional or scintillation counter;

the 11.4-day Ge^{71} decays via an electron capture

and, according to Marinsky, [1] can be indentified

by observing the intensity of the x-rays in a

scintillation counter. The β and γ spectra associated

with the decay of germanium isotopes with mass

numbers 75 and 77 are complex as a result of

isomerism. The internal conversion caused by the

γ radiation complicates the analysis. The use of γ

spectrometers has solved this problem. The as-

signment of activity to a definite isomer and the

evaluation of the fraction of each isomer and isotope

are based on analyses of the γ spectra. [1, 5, 6]

3. Brief Data on Germanium Chemistry Useful
in Radiochemistry

Germanium is characterized by properties inter-

mediate between silicon and tin, on the one hand,

and helium and arsenic on the other.

Under ordinary conditions, metallic germanium

does not react with water, 50% sodium hydroxide,

or hydrochloric, sulfuric and hydrofluoric acid. On

heating, the metal converts to the oxide GeO_2. Germanium dioxide GeO_2 is amphoteric. When it is heated with concentrated hydrofluoric or hydrochloric acid, volatile tetrahalides are formed. The usual method of separating germanium from other elements is the distillation of germanium tetrachloride from a hydrochloric acid solution (6 $\underline{N}$ HCl). When distillation is used, germanium can be readily separated from many elements owing to the low boiling point of its tetrachloride (84°C). When chlorine is bubbled through, the trivalent arsenic (whose chloride can also distil over with germanium chloride) is oxidized to pentavalent arsenic, whose chloride is involatile.

The volatility of germanium chloride makes it impossible to use concentrated HCl or aqua regia for dissolving insoluble germanium compounds, particularly while heating.

Another method of separating germanium consists in its precipitation as the sulfide in a hydrochloric or sulfuric acid solution. This method permits the separation of germanium from all the elements except arsenic, antimony, tin and molybdenum. Like the sulfides of these elements, germanium sulfide is soluble in alkalis, ammonia and sulfide alkalis.

Germanium is not precipitated from solutions containing hydrofluoric or oxalic acid, since it forms stable complexes with them; this permits its separation from arsenic, which precipitates under these conditions. The precipitation of very small quantities of germanium without a carrier (arsenic is the best carrier) is not quantitative.

Germanium coprecipitates with ferric hydroxide when ammonia is employed. This can be used for concentrating it in a small precipitate from large volumes and also for separating it from a large quantity of alkali metal salts. Germanium can be separated from iron by distillation or extraction of the tetrachloride.

Table 2, Distribution Ratio of As(III) and Ge(IV) vs.
Hydrochloric Acid Concentration for Various Solvents
at 30°C

HCl, mole/ liter	Dichloroethyl ether		Benzene		Chloroform		Carbon tetrachloride		Isopropyl ether	
	Ge	As	Ge	As	Ge	As	Ge	As	Ge	As
2,1	0,020	0,012	0,0013	0,001	0,001	0,001	0,0006	0,0010	0,13	0,005
4,2	0,034	0,017	0,026	0,006	0,023	0,01	0,015	0,003	1,3	0,078
6,3	0,63	0,027	0,23	0,17	0,26	0,35	0,24	0,076	17	0,75
8,3	98	2,9	64	4,5	125	3,3	125	1,59	120	1,32
10,3	330	12,5	292	17,7	583	6,9	597	3,7	152	0,30
12,1	309	13,0	434	18,3	630	7,3	594	4,1	221	—

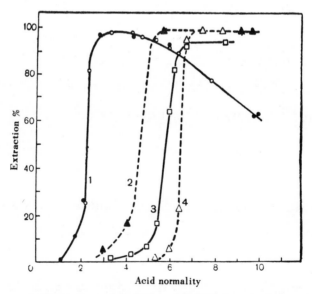

Figure 1, Extraction of As(III) and Ge(IV) from hydrobromic
and hydriodic acid solution with benzene:
1–As/HI;   2–Ge/HI;   3–As/HBr;   4–Ge/HBr

A selective method of separating germanium from interfering elements is the extraction of its tetrachloride by organic solvents. The extraction method of separating germanium is undoubtedly preferable to other methods, for example distillation or precipitation with hydrogen sulfide. It is sufficiently rapid, easy to carry out, and makes it possible to conclude the determination of germanium by any other method. Germanium tetrachloride is extracted from solutions in concentrated HCl by many organic solvents such as chloroform, benzene and aliphatic hydrocarbons, but the best and most convenient solvent is carbon tetrachloride. The extraction of germanium with carbon tetrachloride is carried out from 9 N HCl. Trivalent arsenic is also extracted from HCl with carbon tetrachloride, but with a much smaller distribution ratio (Table 2).

Figure 1 shows graphs of the extraction of arsenic and germanium from hydrobromic and hydriodic acid.

N. P. Rudenko and
L. V. Kovtun

The isolation of germanium by precipitation with tannin is not specific as compared with other methods.

The most difficult part in the isolation of germanium is its separation from arsenic. Many methods can be used for this purpose. In particular, the separation may be achieved by reducing with sodium hyposulfite in an acid solution. Germanium is thus reduced to the divalent state and remains in solution, while arsenic is reduced to the metal, which can be removed by filtering.

The method of reduction of monogermane (GeH_4) by heating to a germanium mirror, similar to the Marsh reaction for arsenic, is of practical importance not only for separation purposes but also for the preparation of samples of radiogermanium. Its separation in the form of a thin, evenly distributed layer by this method can increase the accuracy of measurements of the β emission of germanium isotopes.

Germanium tetrachloride is insoluble in concentrated HCl, and for this reason it can be separated
in greater quantities from solutions containing
arsenic, tin and titanium chlorides by shaking with
concentrated HCl in a separatory funnel.

Ion-exchange resins have not yet been widely
employed in the study of the various properties of
germanium, but we shall nevertheless mention the
method of concentrating germanium from very
dilute   solutions by means of the anion exchanger
EDE-10 and the method of separation from iron,
copper and other heavy metals by means of cation
exchangers. The method of separating germanium
from arsenate and phosphate by means of an anion
exchanger is successfully employed. [1-3,7,21]

4. Methods of Preparation and Separation of
Radioactive Germanium Isotopes

Separation of Radioactive Germanium Isotopes from
Neutron-Irradiated Uranium

Table 1 lists the nuclear reactions from which germanium radioisotopes can be obtained.

To separate radiogermanium, the methods of distillation, extraction, precipitation as the sulfide and certain others are used.

When U^{235} undergoes fission under the influence of neutrons, only short-lived isotopes with a maximum half-life of 11.3 hr are formed. For this reason, the irradiation should not last a long time, and the separation of germanium should be carried out quickly. As a result of their radioactive decay, all the germanium isotopes formed by the fission of U^{235} convert into arsenic isotopes, and the separation from the arsenic must be performed not only when germanium is separated from the mixture of the fission products, but also prior to its use.

The separation of germanium is carried out as follows. A nitric acid solution of irradiated uranyl nitrate with added germanium and arsenic carriers

is evaporated to dryness. The residue is dissolved
in 6 N HCl. When hydrogen is passed through the
solution obtained, germanium and arsenic sulfides
precipitate. The precipitate is removed by centri-
fuging and dissolved in a small amount of concentrated ammonia. The solution is then diluted
with water and zirconium is removed by adding a
zirconium solution as the carrier. The precipitate
which then deposits is separated and discarded.
The solution is acidified with concentrated HCl and
germanium and arsenic sulfide are reprecipitated.
After this last precipitate has dissolved and the
solution is acidified, solutions of tellurium, antimony
and tin carriers are introduced, and germanium
tetrachloride is distilled off by passing gaseous
chlorine. In the distillate, germanium is subjected
to an additional purification by precipitating the
sulfide and distilling off the tetrachloride in the
presence of arsenic, tellurium, antimony and tin.
Finally, germanium is precipitated as the sulfide.

N. P. Rudenko and
L. V. Kovtun

This method has permitted the recovery of germanium of over 99% purity from the fission products of uranium. The decontamination factor relative to other fission products is 10^5.

When germanium is recovered from the fission products, the most difficult problem is that of separating radiogermanium from radioarsenic.

The separation and isolation of these elements can be rapidly accomplished, in addition to the distillation of germanium tetrachloride from HCl solutions, by passing gaseous chlorine and also by using the difference in the chloroform extraction of Ge (IV) and As (III) iodides.

The separation is carried out as follows. To the initial solution, from which nitrate ions were first removed to prevent the oxidation of hydriodic acid, are added solutions of As and Ge carriers. The solution is acidified with HCl up to 3 $\underline{M}$, and, after several ml of 47% hydriodic acid has been added, is

vigorously stirred with chloroform. Arsenic thus
passes completely into the chloroform, while germanium remains in the aqueous layer. To the
aqueous is added 47% hydriodic acid in a volume
about five times that taken for the first extraction,
and the chloroform extraction is repeated. Germanium in the form of GeI_4 passes into the chloroform layer, which is washed with 4 M $HClO_4$ to
remove AsI_3.

As already noted, germanium can be separated
from arsenic by precipitating the latter with hydrogen
sulfide in an HCl solution containing the fluoride ion.
After arsenic sulfide has been separated, the complex
anion GeF_6^{2-} is decomposed by adding boric acid,
and germanium sulfide is precipitated in this solution. A brief separation method consists of the
following: the solution of fission products is acidified with HCl to 3-5 $\underline{M}$, and, after adding the solution of carriers including also germanium (IV),
NaI is introduced (nitrate ions should be absent). The

N. P. Rudenko and
                                        L. V. Kovtun

mixture is carefully heated   and after adding a few
drops of concentrated hydrofluoric acid, the solution
is saturated with hydrogen sulfide until the coagulation
of arsenic sulfide is complete, and the latter is
filtered off. To the filtrate containing germanium
are added several ml of a saturated solution of boric
acid in order to tie up the fluoride ions and saturation
with hydrogen sulfide precipitates germanium as the
sulfide.

Recovery of Germanium from Irradiated Zinc

When zinc is irradiated with α particles, a series
of radioactive germanium isotopes are formed by the
reactions Zn(α, xn)Ge. From these targets, germanium is usually separated with a carrier,
although a separation without a carrier is also possible. A characteristic of these targets and of the
methods of separation of germanium therefrom is
the lack of radioactive arsenic isotopes, which can
form neither as products of the nuclear reaction nor

as products of the radioactive decay of the germanium
isotopes formed. The target material (zinc) should
be very pure.

Thus, the Ge^{65} isotope was obtained as follows.
The target, consisting of zinc (93% of Zn^{64} isotope)
deposited on gold foil, was irradiated with 41 Mev α
particles in a cyclotron. The irradiation lasted from
a few seconds to two minutes. The irradiated target
was dissolved in the presence of the germanium
carrier in a distillation flask in concentrated HCl to
which was added $KClO_3$, which accelerates the dissolution of germanium, and germanium tetrachloride
was distilled off. Since the half-life of Ge^{65} is very
short (1.5 min), the separation must be very fast.

The Ge^{67} isotope was obtained by irradiating chemically pure zinc with 19-Mev α particles for 5-10
minutes. The target was dissolved in a distillation
flask in 8 $\underline{N}$ HCl, germanium and gallium carriers
were added, and the germanium was distilled off in

6 $\underline{N}$ HCl. The germanium was then precipitated as
the sulfide and washed with alcohol and ether.

The Ge^{68} isotope was obtained by irradiating zinc
with ~ 40 Mev α particles. To separate the germanium, the target was dissolved in 6 $\underline{N}$ HCl, germanium
tetrachloride (with the carrier) was distilled off in
3 $\underline{N}$ HCl, and germanium was precipitated as the
sulfide.

Recovery of Ge^{71} from Deuteron-Irradiated Gallium
(the Reaction Ga^{71}(d, 2n)Ge^{71})

Irradiated gallium is dissolved in 48% hydrobromic
acid, and the solution is distilled. Since the boiling
point of GaBr$_3$ is considerably above that of GeBr$_4$
(278.8 and 185.5°C respectively), germanium
bromide distils over with the first few milliliters of
hydrobromic acid. To decompose the latter, the
distilled liquid is evaporated with nitric acid almost
to dryness and, after water has been added, re-
evaporation removes the remainder of nitric acid.

Preparation of Radioactive Germanium Isotopes by

Irradiation of Germanium with Neutrons

When germanium is irradiated with neutrons, the
reaction (n, γ) forms the following radioactive
isotopes: Ge^{71}, Ge^{73m}, Ge^{75}, Ge^{75m}, Ge^{77m} and
Ge^{77}. Of these isotopes, only Ge^{71} and Ge^{77} can
have practical applications, since the remaining
isotopes have very short half-lives. The Ge^{77}
isotope changes into As^{77}, which has a half-life of
1.58 days. It should be kept in mind that this radioactive contaminant is also present in the Ge^{71} preparation. In addition to As^{77}, impurities of the
radioactive isotopes Se^{75}, Sb^{124}, Cs^{134} and Tm^{170}
have also been observed in certain preparations of
radioactive germanium. In order to remove radioarsenic from radiogermanium, in addition to the
above mentioned methods one can use the following
procedure, described for irradiated germanium
dioxide. The irradiated germanium dioxide sample
is dissolved in a sodium hydroxide solution. The

solution is acidified to a concentration of 8 $\underline{M}$ in HCl,
and, in order to achieve a better separation, gaseous
chlorine is passed which oxidizes arsenic to the
pentavalent state. The solution is then passed
through a column of Dowex 1 x 4 anionite treated with
8 $\underline{N}$ HCl. When the column is washed with 3 $\underline{N}$ HCl,
germanium is completely removed, and arsenic re-
mains in the column.

The following purification method is recommended
for the removal of the radioactive impurities Se^{75},
Sb^{124}, Cs^{134} and Tm^{170}. The irradiated germanium, crushed to a powder, is dissolved in a 10%
alkali solution, and 30% hydrogen peroxide is added.
The excess peroxide is then removed by boiling, the
solution is neutralized, acidified with HCl to 9 $\underline{N}$,
then germanium is extracted two to three times with
carbon tetrachloride. Such impurities as antimony,
cesium and rare earths remain completely in the
aqueous phase. To remove the selenium, which has
partly passed into the organic layer, the latter is

washed once or twice with 9 $\underline{N}$ HCl, and germanium
is reextracted from the organic phase into a small
volume of 5 $\underline{N}$ sodium hydroxide. This operation
simultaneously achieves concentration. The germanium yield is no less than 70%.

In order to obtain preparations of high specific
activity, a complex chemical compound of germanium is subjected to neutron irradiation. In the
course of this process, radioactive germanium atoms
separate out of the molecules of the irradiated compound and can be separated from the compound of
nonradioactive germanium. An example of the procedure used to obtain such an enriched preparation
follows.

Tetraphenylgermanium $(C_6H_5)_4Ge$ and
triphenylgermanium fluoride $(C_6H_5)_3FGe$ are irradiated. Into the dioxane solution of irradiated
$(C_6H_5)_4Ge$ is poured an acetone solution of potassium
permanganate after a small amount of hydrogen

N. P. Rudenko and
L. V. Kovtun

peroxide has been added first. The forming manganese
dioxide precipitate occludes the radioactive germanium
atoms. To achieve a better formation of the precipitate, the solution is heated to 60-70°, and the precipitate is filtered off. After washing with water and
acetone, the precipitate can be dissolved in HCl and
germanium tetrachloride can be distilled off.

This method was used to obtain preparations enriched with Ge^{75}, formed by the (n, γ) reaction, and
Ge^{69}, obtained from the (γ, n) reaction during irradiation with synchrotron bremsstrahlung with
255 MeV γ quanta. The yield (recovery)
of Ge^{75} by this method is 91 $\pm$ 4%, and Ge^{69}, 64%.
When triphenylgermanium fluoride is used, the
radioactive germanium is extracted from an ether
solution of the irradiated preparation with an aqueous
solution of sodium fluoride. The yield of radioactive
isotopes in this case is 25-30%.

In the above-described methods used to obtain enriched preparations, the object was to obtain short-

lived isotopes. In order to obtain significant amounts of an enriched preparation of the longer-lived Ge^{71}, a longer irradiation is necessary which causes a substantial breakdown of the irradiated compound and decreases the enrichment. [1, 5, 6, 8-13]

5. Applications of Radiogermanium

Applications in Analytical Chemistry

The lack of radioisotopes with long half-lives and high energy radiation in germanium considerably restricts the scope of its use, particularly in technology.

The Ge^{71} isotope has been used to check the completeness of separation of germanium in the form of germanomolybdic hydroxyquinoline. It should be noted that this compound is used in analytical chemistry for the quantitative determination of germanium. It was found that this method can be used to determine fractions of milligrams of germanium with a maximum error of $\pm$ 3%. To check the complete-

N.P. Rudenko and
                                L.V. Kovtun

ness of the separation, the radioactive isotope Ge^{71}

was added to the sample under analysis prior to the

precipitation. The precipitation was carried out,

and the filtrate separated from the precipitate was

evaporated to dryness. The activity of the evapor-

ated residue was then measured. The same isotope

was then used to check the methods of determining

small quantities of germanium in minerals and coal

ash. It was found that when germanium is recovered

from zinc blende concentrate, the operations of

fusion with sodium peroxide, leaching of the melt,

and precipitation of germanium sulfide from 6 $\underline{N}$

sulfuric and also from 4 $\underline{N}$ hydrochloric acid so-

lutions take place without loss of germanium. The

distillation of germanium tetrachloride in a stream

of chlorine also takes place quantitatively. The

operation of dissolution of the sulfide in ammonia

and particularly of germanium dioxide in water is

associated with certain losses, and the authors of

the work cited[14] established the causes of the

losses and proposed ways of eliminating them. This

method was used to determine 0.054% germanium in
zinc blende concentrate (spectral analysis gave
0.05%) and 0.087% in a sample of brown coal.

Ge^{71} was used to study the coprecipitation of germanium with arsenic (III and V) sulfides. The use
of this isotope was helpful in studying the dependence
of the extent of coprecipitation on the temperature,
concentration of hydrogen sulfide and germanium,
pH of the solution, and presence of complex forming
agents. It was found that the coprecipitation occurs
as a result of the adsorption of germanium on arsenic
sulfide.

Ge^{71} has been used as a radioactive tracer in the
study of the extractive recovery of germanium with
a chloroform solution of 8-hydroxyquinoline. Ge^{71}
was employed in the form of aqueous solutions of
GeO_2 irradiated with slow neutrons. Inasmuch as
during the irradiation short-lived germanium isotopes
Ge^{75} and Ge^{77} are formed together with As^{77}, the

N. P. Rudenko and
L. V. Kovtun

decay product of Ge^{77}, the activity was measured
two weeks after the decay of the short-lived germanium isotopes and As^{77}.

As a tracer, Ge^{71} may find broad applications in
various types of investigations in the chemistry of
germanium and its compounds.

Applications in Technology, Biology and Medicine

To study the behavior of germanium during the
pyrometallurgical processing of sulfide ores containing germanium, the binary sulfide $CuS \cdot GeS_2$
tagged with the Ge^{71} isotope was synthesized. This
isotope was used to elaborate the conditions for the
synthesis of this sulfide.

The physiological effect of germanium is the object
of considerable interest among researchers. However, all the chemotherapeutic studies carried out
up to the present time have yielded indefinite results.
Certain investigators note that germanium compounds
can cause an increase in the number of erythrocytes

and in the content of hemoglobin in the blood of
rabbits. In addition, it was found that in industrial
areas where large quantities of coal are burned,
tuberculosis cases occur less frequently. This is
explained by the beneficial influence of germanium
dioxide, a considerable amount of which is discharged with the smoke. In order to check this
hypothesis, aqueous solutions of germanium dioxide
were introduced orally and intravenously. The oral
administration of 10 mg of germanium dioxide, when
carried out during one day, proved completely harm-
less and even caused an increase in the hemoglobin
content and in the number of erythrocytes. On the
other hand, it was noted that the intravenous administration of supersaturated colloidal solutions of
germanium dioxide caused an immediate collapse
and heart failure.

A number of researchers have established that
there apparently exists a maximum level of germanium in the blood above which the metal either is

not absorbed at all or does not have its usual effect
on the organism. Thus, the physiological action of
germanium compounds is far from clear. For this
reason, radioactive germanium isotopes can also
be successfully used in such investigations.

Activation Analysis

Because of the pronounced negative effect of even
slight quantities of impurities on the semiconducting
properties of germanium, and the fact that germanium is extracted from a raw material where its content is very low, the need has arisen for accurate
methods of determining both minimum quantities of
germanium and the impurities in germanium metal.

The verification of the analysis by chemical or
spectral methods requires considerable preliminary
concentration, which may involve a partial loss of
the impurities, and cause the results to be inaccurate.

The method of radioactivation analysis makes it
possible to solve difficult and even previously insoluble problems of quantitative determination of
minute concentrations of elements.

Thanks to its high sensitivity, this method makes
it possible to perform the analysis without preliminary concentration, and the use of carriers for
the radioactive isotopes obtained permits an evaluation of the degree of separation of traces of elements and the elimination of a special technique
of ultramicroanalysis. The radioactivation method
is very specific, since it is based on the characteristic properties of radioactive isotopes: half-life and
the nature and energy of the radiation. An advantage
of the radioactivation method is the possibility of
determining a series of impurities in a single sample
after carrying out suitable operations of chemical
separation. Since all the chemical operations of
separation and purification are performed after the
irradiation, the purity of the carriers and reagents

used, which plays an important part in ordinary
chemical methods of analysis, is of no particular
importance in this method. Hence, it is not
necessary to introduce corrections for blank
experiments.

The quantitative determination is based on the
fact that the activity and hence the amount of the
radioactive isotope obtained as a result of the nuclear
reaction is related to the amount of the irradiated
element by the expression

$$A_t = \frac{m}{M} \; 6.02 \times 10^{23} \; f\sigma_{act} (1 - e^{-\lambda t}) \qquad (1)$$

where A_t is the number of disintegrations per second
at the instant the irradiation ceases; m is the weight
of the material being analyzed; M is the molecular
weight of the compound or its fraction per atom of the
element being determined; f is the flux level (number
of bombarding particles per cm^2 per second); σ_{act}
is the activation cross section for the activated
isotope of the element being determined; λ is the
decay constant; t is the duration of the irradiation.

The sensitivity of radioactivation analysis depends
mainly on the activation cross section of the element
being determined and on a series of variable factors:
the flux level of the bombarding particles, duration
of the irradiation and half-life of the radioisotope
formed. Thus, the determinable minimum for germanium by means of the reaction (n, γ) for the
Ge^{70} isotope is 3×10^{-11} g; Ge^{74}, 2×10^{-10} g; Ge^{76},
2×10^{-9} g, for a neutron flux of 10^{14} n/cm^2 sec. (1)

A quantitative determination of the content of the
element in the analyzed sample may be made either
by an absolute method of calculation, based on the
use of the above formula, or by a standardization
(comparative) method. The more accurate and
convenient standardization method is customarily
employed. In this method, the amount of the element
in the sample is determined from the relation

$$m_{sample} = m_{std} \frac{A\,sample}{A_{std}} \tag{2}$$

where A are the activities, referred to the same
time, in the sample and standard, irradiated and
measured under identical conditions; m is the content
of the element being determined.

Determination of Copper, Zinc, Molybdenum,
Antimony and Rare Earth Impurities in Metallic
Germanium and Germanium Dioxide

In an analysis of metallic germanium, following
irradiation, a fragment of an ingot weighing about 1
g is treated with dilute (1:1) nitric acid to remove the
activity of foreign elements, whose traces may be
present on the metal surface. The metal is then
crushed in an agate mortar, transferred to a distillation flask (the procedure is exactly the same in
the case of germanium dioxide), and dissolved by
heating in 8 $\underline{N}$ HCl, 10-20 mg of salts of rare earths,
antimony, molybdenum, copper, zinc and also
arsenic (V) having first been added as carriers. The
introduction of arsenic is due to the fact that the

radioisotope As^{77} forms as a result of the nuclear
reaction Ge^{76} (n, γ)$\rightarrow Ge^{77} \rightarrow As^{77}$. After a complete dissolution, the contents of the flask are
evaporated to a volume of 2-3 ml. Evaporation down
to a volume of 2 ml is then carried out three times,
10 ml of concentrated HCl being added each time.
The vapors of HCl and germanium chloride are
absorbed in two gas washing bottles connected in
series and filled with an 8 $\underline{N}$ solution of sodium
hydroxide.

After the bulk of germanium has been distilled off,
the operations of chemical separation and purification
of the analyzed elements are carried out in accordance with the scheme shown in Figure 2.

To prepare the standards, solutions of high-purity
salts of the corresponding elements are taken. The
standards are prepared by introducing trace quantities
of the analyzed element in the form of a solution of a
salt of known concentration into a quartz weighing

N. P. Rudenko and
L. V. Kovtun

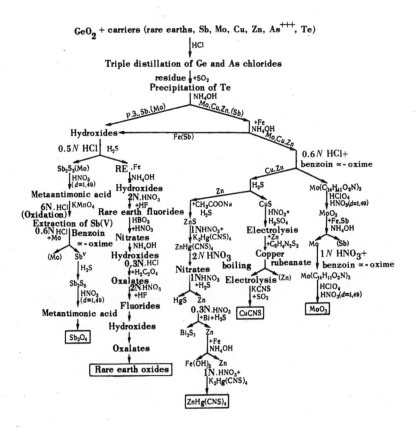

Figure 2, Diagram of chemical separation of analyzed
elements from germanium dioxide

bottle; after drying in a desiccator the standards are
placed in an aluminum container and irradiated
simultaneously with the sample being analyzed. Following the irradiation, the contents of the weighing
bottles are washed out with dilute acid, 5-10 mg of a
suitable carrier is added, and the necessary chemical operations designed to remove the radioactive
impurities of other elements are performed. In
each operation, sodium chloride is introduced as a
"reverse carrier." This is necessary for the removal
of radioactive Na^{24} formed from sodium, which is
usually present in the compounds taken as the
standards.

Analytical chemistry methods are used to determine
the amounts of the separated impurities in the
standard and in the analyzed sample in order to determine their degree of separation.

The radiochemical purity of the separated products
is checked by determining the half-lives or radiation

N. P. Rudenko and
L. V. Kovtun

energies and is compared with tabular data. If the log of the activity changes nonlinearly with time (as for example in the case of total rare earth elements), the curve obtained is analyzed graphically. The nonlinearity may result from the presence of several radioactive isotopes of the same element in the separated product. If the graphical analysis indicates the presence of radioactive isotopes of different chemical elements, it means that the purification was insufficient and should be repeated.

The results of measurements of the activity of all the products separated from the analyzed sample and from the standards should be referred to the same time; corrections for the degree of separation are introduced into the values obtained, and the quantities thus calculated are substituted into the working formula. [2]

Determination of Germanium, Copper, Chromium,
Arsenic and Antimony in Iron Meteorites by Means
of Activation Analysis

The surfaces of the meteorite sample in the form
of fragments measuring 3-4 mm are cleaned with
dilute acid, washed, dried and sealed into small
quartz ampoules. Into the same type of quartz
ampoules, 0.1 ml of the following solutions are introduced: into some ampoules, solutions of arsenic
and antimony containing 0.3 mg As per ml and 0.01
mg Sb per ml; into others, solutions of chromium,
copper and germanium containing 10 mg Cr, 3 mg
Cu and 6 mg Ge per ml. These are the standard
solutions. The ampoules containing them are also
sealed. The ampoules with the samples and solutions
are placed in an aluminum can and irradiated in a
reactor for two weeks.

Following the irradiation, the surface of the samples
is washed with dilute acid and the samples are dissolved in a mixture of hydrochloric, nitric, hydro-

fluoric and perchloric acids in the presence of 20

mg of germanium, 50 mg of arsenic, 40 mg of

antimony, 20 mg of copper and 10 mg of chromium

taken as carriers. On heating until perchloric acid

vapors appear, a complete dissolution of the sample

takes place. The introduction of hydrofluoric acid

prevents the loss of germanium by volatilization.

In the case of troilite samples, the undissolved

residue is fused with sodium peroxide or dissolved

in a mixture of concentrated acids containing hydro-

fluoric acid or fused with $KHSO_4$. After adding an

HCl solution, 5 g of oxalic acid is added, and the

sulfides of copper, arsenic and antimony are

precipitated quantitatively with a 2% solution of

thioacetamide. Germanium is precipitated from the

filtrate by adding 25 ml of a 5% solution of tannin and

neutralizing the solution with ammonia.

The germanium precipitate is treated with HCl and

a solution of hydrogen peroxide, and germanium

tetrachloride is distilled off in the presence of

arsenic, iron, cobalt and copper as reverse carriers. Germanium sulfide is precipitated in the distillate and mounted on an aluminum support to measure the activity with a β counter.

The determination of the germanium content in a meteorite was made by using the Ge^{77} isotope. To determine germanium alone from the formation of this isotope, a shorter irradiation, 10-20 hours, is completely adequate. The germanium content can also be determined from the formation of other isotopes (Ge^{75}, Ge^{71}).

At the present time, it has become largely unnecessary to carry out laborious and long-lasting operations of chemical separation of the radioisotopes formed from the analyzed sample and standards or to determine their quantities by isotopic dilution. Such an improvement of the activation analysis method became possible thanks to the creation of special instruments, multichannel radiation analyzers, which permit the

N. P. Rudenko and
L. V. Kovtun

recording of the radiation spectrum. The recording
and comparison of the radiation spectra of the
analyzed sample and standards following their irradiation make it possible to solve the problem of
formation of the corresponding radioisotope in the
analyzed sample and the problem of quantitative
content of elements from which they were formed.
Such a variant of the method of activation analysis
has been termed the spectroscopic (gamma-
spectroscopic) variant. This variant of the activation
method has made it possible to carry out the analysis
by using shorter-lived radioisotopes, and has
expanded the potential of activation analysis still
further and raised its accuracy. [1, 4, 14-19]

6. Safety Measures in Handling Radiogermanium

According to the "Sanitary Rules of Handling
Radioactive Substances and Sources of Ionizing
Radiations", Ge^{71} is one of the least radiotoxic
isotopes. The maximum permissible concentration
of Ge^{71} in the air of working quarters has been

determined to be 6×10^{-9} C/liter. Radiogermanium
must be handled in protective clothing and rubber
gloves. Special safety measures (lead glass,
plexiglass screen) must be used for protection
against external irradiation if the activity of the
preparation exceeds $0.1 \mu C$.

In quarters where work with radiogermanium is
being done, it is necessary to carry out a daily
cleaning by the wet method. If radioactive substances contaminate the work bench or the floor,
the deactivation must be performed immediately.
If a powder has been spilled, it is collected with a
wet rag that has been wrung out, care being taken
not to smear dry areas. If a liquid has been spilled,
it is soaked up with dry absorbent rags or filter
paper. A large amount of spilled liquid is collected
with dry sawdust. After the bulk of the radioactive
contamination has been removed, the remaining
contamination is eliminated by means of special

wetting agents. The most common and readily avail-

able are the following compositions: (I) 300 ml

Petrov's contact diluted with water up to 1 liter, (II)

a mixture of 300 ml of Petrov's contact, 10 g of

oxalic acid and 50 g of NaCl, diluted with water up to

1 liter. In addition to these agents, a 1% solution of

citric acid can be used for deactivating valuable

instruments. [20]

REFERENCES

1. J.A. Marinsky: The Radiochemistry of Germanium. US Atomic Energy Commission, 1961.

2. H. Remy: Inorganic Chemistry. Vol. 1. IL,
   1963.

3. Concise Chemical Encyclopedia. Vol. I. Moscow, "Sovetskaya entsiklopediya", 1961.

4. O. Johnson: Uspekhi khimii, 25, No. 1, 105
   (1956).

5. B.S. Dzhelepov and L.K. Pekker: Decay
   Schemes of Radioactive Nuclei. Moscow -
   Leningrad, Akad. Nauk SSSR, 1958.

6. A.N. Nesmeyanov, A.V. Lapitskii, and N.P.
   Rudenko: Production of Radioactive Isotopes.
   Moscow, Goskhimizdat, 1954.

7. V.A. Nazarenko: Present State of the Analytical
   Chemistry of Germanium. Akad. Nauk SSSR,
   1959.

8. M.M. Golutvina and E.A. Tikhomirova:
Radiokhimiya, 2, No. 1, 112 (1960).

9. A.N. Murin, V.D. Nefedov, V.I. Baranovskii,
and D.K. Popov: Dokl. AN SSSR, 111, No. 4,
806 (1956).

10. G.H. Morrison and Y.F. Cosgrove: Analyt.
Chem., 28, No. 3, 320 (1956).

11. R.A. Ricci and R. Van Lieshout: Nucl. Phys.,
10, No. 4, 360 (1959).

12. N. Porile: Phys. Rev., 112, No. 6, 1954 (1958).

13. F. Salvetti: Ref. zh. khim., No. 11, 41807 (1960).

14. L.K. Bradacs, I.M. Ladenbauer, and F. Hecht:
Mikrochim. acta, No. 3, 229 (1953).

15. A.N. Baraboshkin: Tr. Ural'skogo politekhn.
in-ta, 81, 166 (1959).

16. N.P. Rudenko and L.V. Kovtun: Tr. Komis. po
analit. khimii AN SSSR, XIV, 209 (1963).

17. I.P. Alimarin, Yu. V. Yakovlev, and A.I.
    Zhabin: Quantitative Determination of Impurities
    in Germanium by Radioactivation Analysis. In:
    Use of Tagged Atoms in Analytical Chemistry.
    Moscow, Akad. Nauk SSSR, 1955.

18. V.I. Davydov and N.P. Diev: Zh. prikl. khimii,
    32, No. 2, 441 (1959).

19. C.C. Harrold, S.F. Meck, and C.P. McCrod:
    Ind. Med. and Surg., 13, 236 (1944).

20. Sanitary Rules of Handling Radioactive Sub-
    stances and Sources of Ionizing Radiations.
    Moscow, Akad. Nauk SSSR, 1955.

21. A. Kjelberg and A. Pappas: J. Inorg. Nucl.
    Chem., 11, No. 3, 173 (1959).

J